THE COUNTRYSIDE BIBLE BOOK

Margaret and Alan

THE
COUNTRYSIDE
BIBLE BOOK

By

DONALD M. McFARLAN, M.A.

Lecturer in Religious Education,
Jordanhill College,
Glasgow

Illustrations by F. T. Holmes

STIRLING TRACT ENTERPRISE

FOREWORD

Donald McFarlan has accomplished here something entirely new. He has taken fifty-two common things from the countryside and linked these up with some corresponding incidents in the Bible. He has thus done two things at the same time—provided a series of nature studies and a fascinating method of scripture-searching. And all with a mind trained to teach the children and a heart tuned to love them. The illustrations by F. T. Holmes help to round off this brilliant effort to break up new ground.

CONTENTS

CONTENTS

CHAPTER ONE

THE COUNTRYSIDE BIBLE BOOK

"OH ! I do like living in the country ! " said Margaret. She and her brother, Alan, sat on the rug in front of the crackling log fire and toasted their toes.

Their mother smiled.

" Why do you like the country, Margaret ? " she asked. " Because it's clean and lovely, and because there are flowers, and woolly lambs, and friendly, munching cows, and . . . oh ! all kinds of things," Margaret replied.

" And fishing, and swimming in the sea, and watching the birds, and helping on the farm," Alan chimed in.

Mr. Richmond looked up from his book.

" Oh ho ! " he said. " *That's* a change of tune ! A few months ago you were sorry enough to leave Glasgow. Remember ? ' Nothing to do and nothing to see in the country.' That's what you said."

Alan grew red. " I know," he confessed. " Don't rub it in ! How was I to know how jolly it would be at Craiglussach ? The country for me, now, every time ! "

The Richmonds lived in a big, old-fashioned manse in the West Highland village of Craiglussach, where Mr. Richmond was minister. It was a Sunday evening. Supper was over, and Margaret and Alan were waiting for their father to tell them the usual Sunday good-night story before they went off to bed. " Just think ! " said Margaret again. " We've only been here three months, and already we know everyone in the village. How strange it would have been to speak to people in the street in Glasgow. Here everyone says ' Good morning ! ' and stops to speak. It's a friendly place."

" And I've seen a fox, and I've caught six trout in the burn," said Alan. " You couldn't do that in smoky, dirty, old Glasgow ! "

" Now, now, Alan ! " said his father. " You mustn't despise the city altogether, you know. But you're right enough in a way. It was a wise man who said : ' God made the country and man made the town.' I think we were meant to live near to God's creatures and to be friendly to our neighbours, and to love wild things."

" Jesus lived in the country, didn't He, Daddy ? " said Margaret.

" Certainly He did. And He was always talking about country things . . . lilies, a farmer sowing his corn, oxen ploughing the fields, a hen and its chicks. Do you remember ? As a matter of fact, the whole Bible is full of beasts and birds and flowers and stories of the countryside."

" Well, I never thought of that," said Alan.

" Just you look and see," replied his father. " I'll tell you what we'll do. Let's make a Countryside Bible Book. Every Sunday night we'll see what the Bible says about animals and birds and all sorts of countryside things."

" And I'll draw pictures of the beasts and the flowers," cried Margaret.

" And I'll look them up in the Bible and find out what it says about them," added Alan.

And so they did. And here is their Countryside Bible Book.

CHAPTER TWO

A LION IN THE SNOW

"SNOW! Snow! Lovely white snow!" chanted Margaret. She stood at the study window with her nose pressed against the pane and watched the snowflakes drifting softly against the house.

"Fine!" said Alan. "I do hope it lasts! We must try out the new sledge to-morrow."

"Was there any snow in the Bible, Daddy?" asked Margaret, as she turned to the cosy fireside again.

"Of course there was!" replied her father. "It's funny you should speak about snow just now. I was thinking that we should start off our Countryside Bible Book with the Lion, because he is the king of beasts. And I've just remembered that a lion comes into the only snowy day mentioned in the whole Bible."

"A lion in the snow!" cried Alan. "Well, that's strange. I always thought lions lived in Africa."

"Oh, there were lions in Palestine, too, long ago," said his father. "They used to make their dens in the forest or on the mountainside, or along the Jordan valley. The shepherds hated them because they came and killed the sheep. Sometimes if they were very hungry they used to roar round the villages.

"One wintry day, when it was snowing, a hungry lion fell into a big pit near a village. The people could hear him roaring in anger, but he couldn't get out. Then one man said that he would go out and kill the lion."

"Who was he?" said Alan eagerly.

"He was a captain of the king's army," answered his father, "and he was already famous as a very brave man."

"He must have been brave to fight a lion," murmured Margaret. Her father went on: "The captain went to the pit and climbed down into it, and killed the lion there. What do you think of that for an adventure? I think the

7

people of that village must have remembered that snowy day for ever afterwards. At anyrate, it's the only snowy day mentioned in the Bible : 'the day the captain slew the lion in the pit.'"

"But that lion was not the only one in the Bible," Mr. Richmond continued. "In fact, when the king heard what the captain of his guard had done he must have remembered an adventure of his own, many years before. He was only a boy at the time, and his father had sent him to watch the sheep. One day, he saw a lion crouching ready to spring. Do you know what he did ? He got between the lion and the sheep. Then the lion snarled at him and sprang. But the shepherd boy seized the beast's mane with one hand and stabbed him with his dagger in the other. And so he killed the lion and saved his sheep."

"I think the shepherd boy was even braver than the captain," said Margaret. "I would have run away !"

"I wonder if you know his name ? " said her father. "And you, Alan, do you think you could find out the name of the captain who slew the lion on a snowy day ? "

CHAPTER THREE

THE LION RIDDLE

ALAN and Margaret were playing at riddles. "Here's one for you," said Alan.

> ' Come a riddle, come a riddle,
> Come a rot-tot-tot ;
> A wee, wee man in a red, red coat ;
> A stick in his hand and a stane in his throat ;
> Come a riddle, come a riddle,
> Come a rot-tot-tot ! '

"I know that one," said Margaret. "The answer is a cherry. I heard it from Mrs. Cameron at the farm last week. She said it was an old Scottish riddle."

"Any riddles in the Bible, Dad ? " asked Alan as they settled down for their Sunday night Bible story. "If you can find a lion in the snow, I expect you'll be able to tell us a Bible riddle, too."

"Certainly," said Mr. Richmond. "The Jews were very fond of making up clever riddles for their friends to guess. As a matter of fact, there's a story in the Old Testament about a lion in a riddle."

"Another lion ! " exclaimed Alan.

"Yes, in a riddle this time, not in the snow," said his father with a smile.

"This story is about a young man who was very strong. One day, when he was going to see the girl he was going to marry, he met a lion. The beast roared at him, and he seized it and killed it with his bare hands. The next time he passed that way he was surprised to see that wild bees had built a hive in the body of the dead lion. He broke off some of the honey-comb and ate it as he went along.

"The time came for the young man's wedding, and there was a great feast, with many guests and games and rejoicing. And at the feast the young man said to the others : ' I'll tell you a riddle.'

> ' From the eater came something to eat,
> From the strong came something sweet.'

"He was thinking, of course, of the lion he had killed. But though the others puzzled their heads for days, they couldn't think of the answer. In the end they cheated. They asked the young man's wife to find out the answer for them. And she begged and begged until he told her. Then she went and told the others. When the time came for the answer to be given, they said :

> ' What is sweeter than honey ?
> What is stronger than a lion ? '

"And the young man was very angry with his wife because she had told the secret."

"What a shame ! " cried Margaret. "I think it was very nasty of her to tell."

"It was a clever riddle," said Alan. "I'd never have thought of the answer if you hadn't told us about the lion first. Who was the strong young man, Dad ? "

"Ah, now you're asking ! " said his father. "That's for you to find out, Alan ! There's a puzzle for you ! "

CHAPTER FOUR

A PRIDE OF LIONS

"I'VE found another Bible lion," announced Alan next Sunday evening. "A whole lot of them, in fact. They come into the story of Daniel . . . 'Daniel in the lions' den.'"

"Good for you!" said Mr. Richmond. "We're collecting quite a pride of lions from the Bible, aren't we?"

"A *what* of lions?" asked Margaret with a puzzled frown.

"A pride," replied her father. "You've heard of a 'flock of sheep,' a 'pack of hounds,' and a 'brood of chickens'? Well, a collection of lions is called a 'pride of lions.' I suppose it is because the lion is so fierce and proud. We always think of it as a kingly animal."

"That must be why it is on the Scottish flag," cried Alan. "And on the Queen's coat of arms," added Margaret.

"The lions in the story of Daniel were royal lions," went on Alan. "But I've always wondered how the king caught them."

"Well, I expect he got them as gifts," said Mr. Richmond. "We know from the Bible that lions chased and killed sheep. Zechariah tells us about the shepherds complaining because the lions have spoiled their flocks. And Amos, who was a sheep-farmer himself, talks about a shepherd finding a lion eating a sheep and all that is left is two legs or a piece of an ear.

"Sometimes the shepherds joined together to hunt the lions. They dug pits and then drove the lions before them by shouting and yelling, until the beasts fell into the pits. Ezekiel speaks of shepherds catching a lion in a pit and tying him up and carrying him off to the king."

"I wouldn't like to keep a lion as a pet," said Margaret.

"No, I'm afraid they were very fierce," said her father. "They were kept in a deep pit, and when the king wanted to get rid of an enemy, he threw him to the lions."

"That's what happened to Daniel," cried Alan.

"Yes, but that time the king was very sorry," said his father. "You see, Daniel was a slave in a land far from his own home. But he never forgot the God of his fathers, the true God. And every evening he opened the windows of his room facing his homeland and prayed to God. His enemies caught him at it. They reminded the king that he had made a law that any man who prayed to anyone except to the king himself was to be killed. So Daniel was thrown to the lions, and the king was very sorry because of his foolish law."

"But the lions didn't eat Daniel after all" said Margaret.

"No, they didn't," answered her father. "Daniel trusted in God, and God sent his angel to shut the lions' mouths, so that he came to no harm."

"I like Daniel," said Margaret. "He was very brave."

"I like him too," agreed her father. "Daniel had the courage of his convictions. He trusted in God, and God didn't let him down. Not all the lions in the world could stop him doing what he knew was right."

"I wonder who the king was," murmured Margaret.

"I wonder !" said her father.

CHAPTER FIVE

THE MEAL GIRNEL

"WE walked miles and miles yesterday," said Margaret. "Right along the canal bank to the lock gates."

"Yes, and we saw a ship going through," added Alan. "We both helped Mrs. Grant to open the lock gates."

Margaret took up the tale. "Mrs. Grant has the cleanest, tidiest cottage you ever saw," she said. "She and her little boy Jock live there all alone. And whenever a ship comes along the canal they run out and open the lock gates to let it through."

"Jock has a funny name," said Alan. "His real name is John Grant, but everyone calls him Jock the Lock because he lives beside the lock on the canal. His father was called Jock the Lock before him because he was lock-keeper there once."

"After the boat was safely through we all went into Mrs. Grant's kitchen for tea," Margaret went on. "She was baking oat-cakes over the fire, all crisp and curly and floury. They *were* good!"

"She had a big barrel of oatmeal in the corner of the kitchen," said Alan. "She called it the girnel. She said that was the proper Scottish name for the meal barrel. And whenever she makes porridge or bakes oat-cakes, she takes the meal from the girnel. She said that she was like the widow woman in the Bible who had a barrel of meal that never failed. What did she mean, Dad?"

"Ah, Mrs. Grant puzzled you with that one, Alan," said his father. "She must have meant the widow woman and her only son at . . . no, I won't tell you where. I'll let you find that out for yourselves. They lived all by themselves like Mrs. Grant and her boy Jock the Lock.

"There came a time of great famine in the land. One hungry day followed another until the poor woman found that she had only a handful of meal left in her meal girnel to feed herself and her boy. On that sad day she was out gathering sticks for the fire, to cook what looked like being their last meal.

"A man approached her. He looked hungry and tired. 'Give me a little water to drink,' he begged. And then he added: 'And a morsel of bread to eat.'

"The widow woman told the stranger that she had only a handful of meal left in the girnel.

"'Don't be afraid,' said the stranger. 'Go and prepare some of the meal for me to eat. The barrel will never be empty in your home until the days of famine are at an end.'

"And so it happened. The stranger, who was a prophet of God, stayed in the house of the widow woman and her son for many days, and there was always enough meal in the girnel to give them food. Day by day, God supplied their needs."

"I see now what Mrs. Grant meant," said Alan. "She has always some meal in her girnel for herself and Jock the Lock."

"And a share for strangers, too," Margaret reminded him.

"Can I find out the name of the woman in the Bible, Daddy?"

"No," said her father. "Her name isn't given. But the Bible does tell you where she lived. And Alan can find out the name of the stranger prophet whom she made welcome to her humble home."

CHAPTER SIX

THE TENT-MAKER

" I SAW the tinkers arriving yesterday," announced Alan one Sunday evening. "They're camping in the old quarry behind the Camerons' farm. They've got a horse and cart, and they all sleep in an old brown tent."

"But the young ones are busy making tents of their own from branches of trees covered with sacking," said Margaret. "They must feel very cold sometimes when the wind blows through the gaps at night. But they had a big, crackling, log fire, too," she added. "The camp looked quite cosy."

"I'm going to make a tent like that when the Summer comes," said Alan. "Jim Cameron showed me the very place for it, in the shelter of the bridge down near the mouth of the burn."

"You're a son of Jabal, Alan," smiled his father. "The Bible says that ' he was the father of such as dwell in tents.' "

Alan grinned. "I knew you would find a tent in the Bible, Dad," he said. "Tell us about some of them."

"Well, that's a tall order," said his father. "There are hundreds upon hundreds of tents in the Bible. For many, many years the children of Israel were a wandering people, shepherds and cattle-owners. They carried their homes, their tents, with them wherever they went. Abraham and Isaac and Jacob were all tent-dwellers."

"They must have had tents when they were wandering in the wilderness," said Margaret.

Her father nodded his head. "Not only that," he agreed, "but their church was a tent also. It is called the Tabernacle in the Bible, but the word ' tabernacle ' just means a tent. Wherever they went they took their tent-church with them and pitched it in the midst of their camp."

"What were their tents made of ? " asked Alan.

"Sometimes of skins, and sometimes of woven goats' hair," replied his father. "And sometimes they were like the young tinkers' tents, made of woven branches with cloth tied over the top.

"There is a famous tent-maker in the New Testament," Mr. Richmond went on. "He was a young man who came from a well-to-do family, and he received a very good education. After he had finished school in his home town of Tarsus, he crossed the sea to Palestine and studied under the learned teachers in Jerusalem. It was there that he first met the followers of Jesus, and later he, too, became one of His disciples.

"But this clever young man was not only a scholar. Like all Jewish children, he had been taught to work with his hands, so that he could earn his living by his trade, if need be. His trade was tent-making, and wherever he went as a missionary of Jesus Christ he wove goats' hair tents to pay for his keep. He was a burden to no one. 'These hands,' he said once, ' have served my needs.'

"Now, Alan and Margaret, there's something to interest you ! I wonder if you can find out the name of the scholar who was also a missionary and a tent-maker ? "

CHAPTER SEVEN

THE YOUNG PLOUGHMAN

" A HALF-HOLIDAY from school to-morrow!" said Alan. "And, Dad, Jim Cameron has invited me up to the farm for the night. He's going to help his father to plough the big field to-morrow afternoon, and I want to help, too."

Mr. Richmond smiled. "I don't think it's the hard work of ploughing that interests you," he said. "It's the new tractor."

"Isn't it a beauty!" cried Alan, his eyes sparkling. "Jim says it will do twice as much work as the horses. And it never gets tired."

"But sometimes it breaks down," said his father mischievously. "And then, no doubt, the pair of you will be crawling about underneath, getting all oily and dirty trying to make it go again."

"I like the horses best," said Margaret. "Perhaps they are old-fashioned, but they are friendly beasts and it's lovely to watch them pulling together. Who could make friends with a noisy old tractor?"

"Now, now, you two!" said Mr. Richmond. "No arguing! I must confess I love to watch the horses working over the land. But the tractor is fine, too, a gleaming, red monster eating up the furrows like a dragon."

"What did the Bible folk use for ploughing?" asked Margaret. "Of course, they didn't have tractors. Did they use horses?"

Mr. Richmond shook his head. "No," he said, "when we read about horses in the Bible they were usually used for fighting. For the peaceful work of ploughing the Jews used a pair of oxen, or sometimes asses. And that reminds me. There's a story in the Old Testament about a young man ploughing a field which I think will interest you.

"The story really begins with Elijah the prophet. He was very sad because it seemed to him that no one wanted to listen to the Word of God. So he went into the wilderness and sulked. But God spoke to him there.

" 'What are you doing here, Elijah!' He said. And the prophet answered sadly : ' I am very sorrowful. I alone am left of all Thy people, and no one will listen to me.'

"But God said : ' No ! There are still thousands of faithful folk in Israel. Get back to your work. I have much for you to do.'

"So Elijah went on his way, and, as he was going along the country road, he saw a young man ploughing on his father's farm among the farm labourers. He knew him to be a fine young man, and the sight gave Elijah new courage.

" ' There's a man for the work of God,' he thought to himself. And he threw his cloak over the young man's shoulders for a sign that he should be God's servant. The young man was greatly disturbed. He left the plough and ran after Elijah.

" ' Let me say goodbye to my father and mother,' he cried. ' Then I will follow you.'

"Elijah spoke gently to him. ' Don't be afraid,' he said. ' Go on with your work. In God's good time you will do His work.' "

"And did he ? " asked Margaret.

"Yes," said her father. "He came to be like a son to Elijah, and later he was the great prophet of God in Israel. I wonder if you can find out who the young ploughman was ? "

CHAPTER EIGHT

THE FIRST LAMB

"DO you know what I saw yesterday, Daddy?" said Margaret. "The first, the very first, of the new lambs. Poor little thing, it looked so weak and cold. It was born in the field beside the farm, and Mrs. Cameron took it to the kitchen and wrapped it up in an old coat. It looked so funny with just its head sticking out. And she let me feed it, too, from a baby's feeding-bottle. It sucked down all the milk, and then started to lick my fingers. Mrs. Cameron says I can come up to see it whenever I like."

"Jim Cameron says that the shepherd at the farm is the best in Argyll," said Alan. "Sometimes he's out all night in the lambing season, looking after the sheep and the newly-born lambs."

"I always think that the Spring is the happiest time of the year," said Mr. Richmond, "when we see the new lambs, all white and curly, skipping about and playing among the daisies on the hill-side. Then everyone knows that Spring is really here."

"I'm sure there are lambs in the Bible," said Margaret. "Can you tell us a story about them to-night, Daddy?"

"Yes, there are many, many lambs in the Bible," said her father. "The Jews were a shepherd people, and they kept great flocks of sheep. Joseph, you remember, was a shepherd boy. So was David, who became king of Israel. He used to watch over the flocks, Alan, just like your friend the shepherd at the farm, to protect them from harm. Once he saved his lambs from a lion, and once from a bear. And he must have enjoyed watching the young lambs playing, because in one of the Psalms which he wrote he says, 'The mountains skipped like rams, and the little hills like lambs.'"

"I've just remembered something," said Alan. "Jesus was called 'the Lamb of God,' wasn't He, Dad? I wonder why?"

19

"I think it was because He spoke of peace and love among men who very often were fierce and envious and quarrelsome. He was pure and peaceable, and harmed no-one. I wonder if you know who called Jesus 'the Lamb of God'? It was a prophet who was preaching by the banks of the river Jordan. When he saw Jesus coming one day, he said to two of his friends: 'Behold the Lamb of God.' At once they were curious to know more about Jesus, and they went after Him. He turned round and said: 'What are you looking for?' And they answered: 'Where are you living, Master?' Then Jesus said to them: 'Come and see!' And they went with Him and stayed with Him that night. We don't know what they talked about, but we do know that one of them, at least, became a disciple of Jesus and followed Him to the end."

"It's a lovely name, 'The Lamb of God'," said Margaret softly. "It's . . . it's so peaceful."

"Yes, because Jesus was the Prince of Peace," answered Mr. Richmond. "Can you find out for me who gave Jesus the name: 'Lamb of God'?"

CHAPTER NINE

THE GOOD SHEPHERD

"WELL, how is your little lamb getting on at Inverbaan farm?" asked Mr. Richmond next Sunday.

"Oh, Daddy, it's growing big and strong, now," said Margaret. "And the big field beside the farm is full of little lambs with their mothers. You were quite right about the skipping. Sometimes two of them chase each other across the field, and then, suddenly, they start skipping about and springing up and down. The shepherd says that this has been a good year for lambs."

"He takes great care of them," Alan added. "And the funny thing is that none of the sheep is afraid of him. They all seem to trust him and know that he is looking after them. He's a good shepherd."

"'The Good Shepherd!'" repeated Mr. Richmond. "That's another of the names of Jesus, Alan. He gave Himself that name. He said: 'I am the Good Shepherd, and know my sheep, and am known of mine.' And He tells how the Good Shepherd calls his own sheep by name, and leads them out. But they will not follow a stranger, because they don't know the stranger's voice.

"Jesus told a story about a good shepherd once," Mr. Richmond went on. "It was about a man who had a hundred sheep. One day when he counted them, one was missing. Ninety-nine were there in the flock, but one was gone. Do you know what the shepherd did? He left the ninety-nine safely grazing and went to look for the missing one. He had to search for a long time. But at last he found it, the foolish, straying sheep. And the shepherd was overjoyed. He laid it on his shoulders and carried it gently home. Then he called his friends and neighbours and told them all about it, and they rejoiced with him because he had found the sheep that was lost.

"Jesus calls us His sheep and His lambs," Mr. Richmond continued. "He gave a command to one of His disciples, a man who had run away when his Master was crucified. It was a sign that Jesus forgave him, and still trusted him.

The disciple was a fisherman, and Jesus met him with some of the other fishermen on the sea-shore. They sat down together and ate a meal of fish and bread cooked over an open fire of sticks. Then Jesus turned to the disciple who had failed Him.

"'Do you love Me?' He said.

"'Lord, you know that I love Thee,' said the fisherman.

"'Feed My lambs,' said Jesus, 'and feed My sheep.' And after that, the disciple was always true to Jesus and became the leader of all His followers, His sheep and His lambs. I wonder if you know who the fisherman-disciple was? And do you know this good-night prayer to Jesus, the Good Shepherd? :

> 'Jesus, tender Shepherd, hear me;
> Bless Thy little lamb to-night;
> Through the darkness be Thou near me;
> Watch my sleep till morning light.'

CHAPTER TEN

THE ADDER

"JIM CAMERON killed an adder near the hen-house this morning," said Alan. "His mother saw it when she went out to feed the hens, and she shouted for Jim. He says it was about twenty inches long. Jim told me all about it at Sunday School to-day. He's going to keep the skin as a souvenir."

Margaret shivered. "I wouldn't like to meet a live adder," she said. "Nor see its skin either. Nasty, dangerous creatures!"

"I don't like them either," agreed Mrs. Richmond. "I'm always afraid that I'll tread on one when I'm going through the heather to Miss MacVicar's cottage."

"I wouldn't be afraid," boasted Alan. "I'd break its back with a stick and then it couldn't do any harm."

Mr. Richmond looked up from his book. "Well, it seems we all know what to do when we meet an adder," he said, with a twinkle in his eye. "Margaret and her mother would run away, and you, Alan, would break its back with a stick —if you had a stick handy, of course!"

"You're teasing us, Daddy!" Margaret protested. "What would *you* do if you met an adder?"

"I'm not sure," confessed her father. "I don't like the idea of killing a living creature unnecessarily. Usually when you see an adder on the hill-side it is out enjoying the warmth of the sun. And it is beautiful, too, in its own way. But it is true enough that they are dangerous creatures, so perhaps Alan is right after all. The bite of an adder is very poisonous.

"There's a story in the Bible about a man who was attacked by a snake while he was gathering firewood," Mr. Richmond went on. "He was a prisoner being taken to Rome for trial because he was a follower of Jesus. But the voyage to Italy was very stormy, and on the way the ship was wrecked. Everyone made for the shore, soldiers and

23

prisoners, sailors and passengers. Not one of them was lost. Those who could not swim clung to broken pieces of the ship, and so everyone came at last to the beach, wet and weary.

"The Bible calls the island on which they landed, Melita. We know it as Malta to day, and you can find it on the map of the Mediterranean. It was raining, and the shipwrecked folk felt very cold and miserable. But the people of the island were kind to them. They gave them shelter, and kindled a warm, cheery fire.

"The Christian prisoner was busy gathering sticks for the fire when, suddenly, a poisonous snake came out of the heat and fastened on his hand. The islanders were horrified. They thought he must be a very evil man. By good luck he had escaped from the sea, and now the snake had been sent to kill him. They waited to see him drop dead.

"But the prisoner just shook off the snake into the fire, and felt no harm. God was looking after him. And during the days he was on the island the people came to know him not as an evil man, but as a follower of Jesus, as he went about healing the sick, and praying, and preaching. I wonder if you know who the prisoner was?"

CHAPTER ELEVEN

BREAD RATIONS

"I'M going into Invergair to-morrow," said Mr. Richmond one Sunday night. "Is there anything you want me to buy?"

"Well, you can pick up the rations if you like," said Mrs. Richmond. "But don't forget to take the ration books. (This, of course, was before May, 1954.)

Mr. Richmond smiled. "I won't forget them," he promised. "But I'm afraid I can never make out what all those pages of letters and numbers mean. I'll just have to trust to the honesty of our friends, the butcher and the grocer."

"Well, I'm sure you can't find rationing in the Bible," said Margaret. "That's one modern invention that the children of Israel were never troubled with!"

"You're wrong there!" cried her father. "Rations are mentioned more than once in the Bible. If you like, I'll tell you to-night about a man who got his rations every day."

"That's a puzzler," said Alan. "I'm sure I've never heard of him before. Go on, Dad."

"He was a great prophet," Mr. Richmond went on. "One of the greatest in the whole story of the Jewish nation. But like all great prophets he wasn't always very popular. He foretold that the city of Jerusalem was going to be destroyed by the powerful enemies of the Jews, the Chaldeans. The rulers didn't believe him, and they were furious at his words. They trusted to the Egyptian army which was marching to their aid.

"'The Chaldeans will run away as soon as they hear that the Egyptians are coming to our rescue,' said the king and his counsellors.

"'Don't deceive yourselves!' said the prophet. 'God has told me to tell you that the Egyptians are turning back to their own land. The Chaldeans will return and defeat you, and they will destroy Jerusalem by fire.' But no one believed him.

"One day the prophet set out to visit his native village some miles from Jerusalem. But he got no further than the city gate. He was stopped there by the sentry, who challenged him. 'You're a traitor!' said the sentry. 'You're trying to slip out to join your friends the Chaldeans!'

"'It's a lie!' said the prophet indignantly. But the sentry would not listen to him. He arrested the prophet, and took him to the authorities who ordered him to be flogged and flung into an underground dungeon.

"But the king was worried about what the prophet had foretold, and he sent secretly for him.

"'Is there any news from the Lord?' he asked.

"'There is!' was the reply. 'You are going to fall into the hands of the enemy!'

"The king decided to keep an eye on the prophet. He didn't put him back in the dungeon where he might die of neglect. He put him in the guard-house. And every day, by the king's special orders, the prophet got a ration of bread from the street of the bakers."

"And did he escape?" asked Alan.

"I think we'll leave his other adventures until next week," said Mr. Richmond. "But I wonder if you can find out before next Sunday the name of the prophet who drew his daily bread ration while he was in prison?"

CHAPTER TWELVE

OLD CLOTHES

"WELL, have you found out the name of the prophet who got his bread ration in prison every day ? " said Mr. Richmond.

"Yes, we have," said Margaret. "He was Jeremiah, and the name of the king was Zedekiah."

"But it took us a long time to find him," added Alan. "You promised you would tell us what happened next, Dad. Did Jeremiah get out of prison ? "

"Yes, he did, for a time," said Mr Richmond. "But soon he was put back into a deep dungeon again. The rulers of the city wanted to kill him. 'He says that the city will be destroyed,' they cried, 'and his words are taking the heart out of our citizens and soldiers.' The king was not strong enough to stand up to them. 'He is in your hands,' he said.

"So the authorities took Jeremiah and flung him into a deep underground cistern, and left him to die. Fortunately, there was no water in the cistern, or he would have drowned at once. But it was bad enough. The bottom of the cistern was soft mud, and Jeremiah sank down in it. In the darkness of the pit there was neither food nor drink, no light, and, seemingly, no one to help. It looked as if the end had come.

"But Jeremiah was not without a friend. There was an African servant in the palace who heard what they had done to Jeremiah. He went at once to the king.

"'Your majesty,' he said, 'these men have done great evil to the prophet Jeremiah. They have cast him into a cistern, and he will die there of starvation, for there is no food left in the city.'

"So the king ordered the African to take some men with him and pull Jeremiah out of the cistern before he died."

"Good for the Negro ! " cried Alan. "This *is* an exciting story, Dad."

"The African didn't go straight to the cistern," Mr.

27

Richmond went on. "He did a very kind and thoughtful thing. He went first to a lumber-room in the palace and raked out a bundle of old clothes and soft rags . . . 'cast clouts,' the Bible calls them. Then he lowered them by ropes into the dark pit where the prophet was, and called out : 'Put them under your armpits so that the rope won't hurt you.'"

"That *was* a thoughtful thing to do," said Margaret. "I expect Jeremiah was glad of the rags to tie under the rope after all that he had suffered."

"Well, they pulled him up," Mr. Richmond went on. "He must have been weak with hunger and filthy with mud. But I expect he thanked God that he saw the light of day once again."

"And was he set free ? " asked Alan.

"No, I'm afraid not," said his father. "But he lived once again in the guard-room. It wasn't long before the city fell to the enemy, just as Jeremiah had foretold all along. The enemy set him free, but the king and the rulers were carried off in chains to exile."

"What happened to the African ? " asked Alan.

"He was saved, too," said his father, "because of his kindness to Jeremiah. Do you think you can find out his name ? "

CHAPTER THIRTEEN

MARCH WINDS

"OH! Oh! I'm being blown away by the wind!" cried Margaret. "Give me your hand, Daddy."

Margaret and Alan were out for a walk with their father. It was a wild and windy March day. Every moment or two a gust of wind swept up the loch and caught at their coats. It made their cheeks glow and their fingers tingle as they struggled homewards with heads bent against the blast.

"I . . . can . . . scarcely . . . breathe!" gasped Alan. He swung round and began to walk backwards. "There! That's better! What a wild day! Look, Dad, the white horses are out all over the loch. I wouldn't like to be out in a boat in this weather!"

The three of them stood for a moment watching the gale stirring up the surface of the loch into white foam and spray.

"It's a wild day all right," agreed Mr. Richmond. "And it looks like being a wild night. Real March weather."

> 'March winds and April showers
> Bring forth May flowers,'

chanted Margaret. "Come on, Alan, I'll race you home. I wish the wind was at our backs instead of against us. Then I could spread out my coat and fly home like a bird!"

The study fire that night was warm and friendly. Outside, the storm battered at the windows in angry gusts, or howled round the chimney tops.

"There was a gale warning on the wireless to-night," said Mr. Richmond. "The fishermen will be having a hard time of it. Do you remember the Bible story about the storm on the loch, Margaret and Alan?"

"A storm on a loch?" repeated Alan. "I didn't think there was a loch in the Bible."

"Well, loch is our Scottish word for 'lake'," said Mr. Richmond, "but it means exactly the same thing. There is a story about Jesus and his disciples in a storm on the lake."

"The lake was calm enough when they set out," Mr.

29

Richmond went on, "and several of the disciples were fishermen, so they knew how to handle a boat. Jesus was very tired, so He lay down in the stern and went to sleep. But, after a bit, a sudden storm swept down on the lake, and soon the disciples were in difficulties. Try as they would, they could make no headway at all, and the raging waves began to sweep over them. The boat was filling with water, and it looked as if they might all drown.

"Some of them scrambled to the stern of the boat where Jesus was still sleeping peacefully. They shook Him awake.

"'Master, Master, we perish!' they cried.

"And Jesus sat up, and looked around. He spread out His arms towards the raging waters.

"'Peace, be still,' He said.

"And immediately the wind hushed and the waters sank to rest. The storm was over, at His word.

"The disciples were afraid. 'What kind of man is this?' they said to one another. 'He commands even the winds and water and they obey Him!'"

"I hope Jesus will look after the fishermen in the storm to-night," said Margaret. "What do you want us to find out this week, Daddy?"

"Well, what was the name of the lake, or 'loch—' as we call it?" asked her father.

30

CHAPTER FOURTEEN

THE FOUR FISHERS

"WHAT a difference from last Sunday!" said Mrs. Richmond. "It's as quiet to-night as a Summer evening. The gale must have blown itself right out."

"March comes in like a lion and goes out like a lamb," quoted Mr. Richmond. "Now, I suppose, we must expect April showers. But not too many of them, I hope!"

"I wonder how the fishermen got on," said Alan. "I expect they had plenty to tell about the storm when they got safely home again."

"They were very glad to get into harbour," agreed his father. "I saw the fishing fleet tied up in Invergair last Tuesday. The boats had had a battering all right. Most of the men were busy patching and painting and getting ready for sea again. One of the boats had its mast snapped right off. But the nets suffered most of all. One of the fishermen told me they would have to spend most of this week getting them in order again. They were all tangled and torn."

"That reminds me of last Sunday's story," said Margaret. "We found out the name of your 'loch,' Daddy. It was the lake of Galilee."

"I'd like to hear more about the fishermen," said Alan. "Did they use nets like the fishermen of Lochgair? Or did they fish with line and hook as I do on the loch?"

"They used nets as a rule," replied his father. "As a matter of fact, they were hard at work when Jesus first called them to be with Him. Jesus was walking along the shore of the lake of Galilee one day when He saw them. There were two pairs of brothers, and all four were fishers.

"The first two were out on the water, casting a net. When they came to land, and had beached their boat, Jesus said to them: 'Come with me, and I will make you fishers of men.' And the two fishermen tied up their boat and went with Him.

31

"A little further along the shore the other two brothers were working. They were partners in the fishing business with the first pair of fishers. It must have been quite a prosperous business, because the Bible tells us that their father was working with them too, as well as a number of hired men. When Jesus came along the beach they were busy mending their nets. Perhaps they had been out in a storm, like the Invergair fleet. Jesus called to them, and asked them to come with Him. And they also left their nets and went after Him. These four fishers were the first of His disciples, and they were with Him always after that."

"'The four fishers,'" said Margaret thoughtfully. "You must find out the first pair of brothers, Alan, and I'll find the names of the other two."

"I'll give you a hint," said Mr. Richmond. "One of the four fishers is the patron saint of Scotland. You ought to know his name."

CHAPTER FIFTEEN

THE LOST ASSES

"WE heard about a Bible animal in Sunday School to-day," said Margaret one Sunday night. "The teacher told us that this is Palm Sunday, and we read the story of Jesus riding into Jerusalem on an ass."

"I wonder why people talk about ' a silly ass '," said Alan, thoughtfully.

"Or a ' stupid donkey '," added Margaret.

"No one seems to be very polite to the ass," Mr. Richmond agreed. "But he's a useful beast, all the same, and the Bible folk thought a lot of him. There were no motor cars or trains in those days, and asses were used to carry people and their baggage whenever they went on a journey. They were even used for ploughing the fields."

"Do you know any Bible stories about the Ass ? " asked Alan.

"Yes, several," said his father. "And I think the strangest one is about a young man who went to look for some strayed asses and found a kingdom instead.

"His father was a well-to-do man, as we would say, and the young man himself was a big, strong chap, easily a head taller than anyone else in the country. One day his father called him. ' Son,' he said, ' I'm worried about some of the asses that seem to have strayed. Take one of the servants with you and go and look for them.'

"So the young man packed up some food and he and the servant set off. They went over the hills and down the other side, and up again, scouring the countryside. But even after three days of searching, there was still no sign of the missing beasts. At last the young man said to the servant : ' I think we'd better make for home again. By this time my father will have stopped worrying about the asses. He'll be worrying about me instead ! '

"' Before we turn back,' said the servant, ' let's ask in the village down there. There is a man of God living there who may be able to help us.'

33

"So the pair of them went into the village and asked their way to the house of the man of God. And, sure enough, when they had explained their errand, the man of God told them that their asses had been found."

"How did he know?" asked Margaret.

"God had told him," answered her father. "And God told him also that the young man was coming to see him. The pair of them stayed to dinner with the man of God and spent the night there. Next morning he went along the road with them for a little way. 'Tell your servant to go on ahead,' he said to the young man. 'I have a message from God for you.' Then he put oil on the young man's head and kissed him, and said: 'God has chosen you to be king over His people Israel!'"

"What a surprise for the young man!" said Alan. "Fancy going to round up some stray beasts and coming home a king!"

"I wonder who the tall young man was?" mused Margaret.

"And the man of God?" asked her father.

CHAPTER SIXTEEN

THE LAME MAN'S ASS

"I KNOW who the tall young man in last Sunday's story was," said Alan. "His name was Saul, and he became the first king of Israel."

"And I've drawn a picture of him climbing the hill to look for his father's asses," Margaret added.

"Well," said Mr. Richmond, "I've just remembered that an ass comes into the story of Saul's grandson. Poor chap, he was lame in both feet, so I expect he had to use an ass quite a lot to get about."

"Did he have an accident ? " asked Margaret.

"Yes," said her father. "It happened when he was only five years old. There was fierce fighting in the land, and news came that his father Jonathan and his grandfather the king had been killed in battle. At once the little boy's nurse snatched him up and ran to hide. But in her hurry she dropped him, and his feet were hurt. He never walked properly again."

"Do tell us what happened," said Margaret. "Did he escape from his enemies ? "

"Yes, he did," said her father. "And David the new king was very kind to him because he himself had been Jonathan's closest friend. He saw to it that the boy had a home and servants to look after him, and the boy was made welcome at all times in the king's house."

"Oh, I'm glad," said Margaret. "What a kind thing of the king to do."

"But where does the ass come in ? " asked Alan.

"That was later in the story," went on his father. "David the king had to flee from the capital because of his enemies. And on his way he met the chief servant of the lame man. The servant was leading two asses loaded with bread and raisins and other fruits.

" ' What are you doing with these ? ' asked the king.

"The man bowed low. 'They are a gift for your majesty,' he replied.

35

"'And where is your master?' David enquired.

"'He has stayed behind in Jerusalem,' said the man. 'He hopes that he will be made king now that you have gone.'"

"What an ungrateful rascal!" Alan broke in. "What did the king do?"

"Well, it's a bit of a puzzle to know whether the servant was speaking the truth or not," said his father. "Some time passed, and David won his battles and came home victorious. And whom should he meet but the lame man to whom he had been so kind.

"'Why didn't you leave the city and come with me?' the king demanded.

"'My lord king,' was the reply, 'my servant played me false. I told him to saddle an ass for me, because, as you know, I can't walk. But he went off by himself and told you lies against me. But now my great happiness is that my lord the king has come back safely to his throne again!'"

"And did the king believe him?" asked Alan.

"I'm not sure," said his father. "But he forgave him anyway."

"He must have been a great king," said Margaret. "But I'm sorry for the poor lame man. I don't think he meant to deceive the king."

Her father smiled. "Well, if the king gave him the benefit of the doubt, I think we should, too," he said. "Do you know the lame man's name?"

CHAPTER SEVENTEEN

THE ASS WHICH SAVED A BOY'S LIFE

MARGARET and Alan and their mother were alone in the Manse. Mr. Richmond had gone to preach in Glasgow, and would not be back until Monday night.

"I'll need to join in your Countryside Bible Book to-night," said Mrs. Richmond. "I'd like to tell you another story about an ass. And it's a story about a mother, too."

"What would you call your story?" asked Margaret. "It must have a name, you know."

"I think I'd call it: 'The Ass which saved a boy's life'," Mrs. Richmond replied.

"The woman I'm going to tell you about was a farmer's wife," Mrs. Richmond went on. "She and her husband had a comfortable home and plenty of servants. One day she heard that a man of God was passing that way, so she invited him to take food at the farmhouse. As they talked, she learned that he had been a farmer himself once, but that God had called him to be a prophet. She told him that every time he passed that way he should come and stay with them. And she got the servants to build a little room for him, with a bed and a table and a chair and a lamp, so that he could rest whenever he came.

"One day a terrible thing happened. It was harvest time, and the woman's little boy, her only child, was out playing in the fields among the reapers. It was very hot under the blazing Eastern sun. Suddenly, the little boy began to cry: 'Oh my head! My head!'

"His father told one of the reapers to carry him to his mother. She nursed him in her arms and put cool, wet cloths on his fevered head. But in the middle of the day he died."

"Poor mother!" said Margaret softly. "What did she do?"

"She didn't waste any time," said Mrs. Richmond. "She carried her little son to the prophet's room and laid him on the bed. Then she ran to her husband.

"'Quick!' she said. 'Give me one of the young men to go with me, and tell him to saddle an ass. I'm going to find the man of God.'

"She set off at top speed, driving the ass as fast as it would go. She knew that it was a race for a life, her boy's life. All hot and dusty, she galloped to Carmel, where the prophet was living. The woman jumped down and told him what had happened. And the prophet sent his servant ahead of him and came himself with the mother to the farm-house.

"The man of God went up to the room which had been made for him. Then he prayed to God. He stretched himself over the child's cold body, putting his mouth to the boy's mouth, his eyes upon his eyes, his hands to his hands. And as he lay there, the heat of his body warmed the boy's body. Then the prophet walked quickly up and down the room to warm himself, and lay down again. Suddenly, the child sneezed. One! Two! Three! Four! Five! Six! Seven! Seven times he sneezed, and opened his eyes. And the prophet called his mother and gave her the boy alive and well again."

"I like that mother," said Margaret. "She was so brave and trusting. What was her name, Mummy?"

"I don't know," said Mrs. Richmond. "The Bible doesn't tell us. But it does tell us the name of the man of God. I wonder if you can find that out?"

CHAPTER EIGHTEEN

MAY DEW

"TO-DAY has been a lovely day," said Margaret. "The first day of Summer. Look, the sun isn't even down behind the hills yet!"

They all stood for a moment at the study window watching the evening sun go down the sky. It lit up the hills with a golden glow, and it seemed as if all the flowers in the garden turned to bid the sun goodnight.

"You should have been up early this morning, Margaret, to wash your face in the May dew," said her mother. "Then you would have been beautiful all the year round!"

"Instead of just plain ordinary, as you are just now," added Alan mischievously. Margaret made a face at him.

"There was certainly plenty of dew on the grass when I went out early this morning," said Mr. Richmond. "My shoes were soaking."

Margaret laughed. "The dew wouldn't make your shoes beautiful, anyway," she said.

"No, I'm afraid not," confessed her father. "But everything else in the world looked lovely, all washed clean in the sweet May dew."

"Where does the dew come from every morning?" asked Alan.

"That's a mystery," his father answered. "You are asking what Job asked, Alan, long, long ago. He said: 'Hath the rain a father? or who hath begotten the drops of dew?'

"I think we must have a dew story to-night," Mr. Richmond went on. "It is about the time when the children of Israel were settling down in the land of Canaan. But their enemies, the Midianites, were very strong, and the Israelites were forced to live in caves and dens in the mountains. One day, a young man was busy threshing wheat, trying to keep it hidden from the Midianites, when he had a strange adventure. Suddenly an angel of God stood by him and said : 'The Lord is with thee, thou mighty man of valour.'

"The young man was very much afraid, but he plucked up courage to say : 'O my Lord, if the Lord is with us, why are we in all this trouble ? ' And the angel looked at the young man and said : 'God has chosen you to save Israel ! '

"The young warrior did as God had told him. He called out the tribesmen of Israel by the sound of a trumpet, and prepared to fight the enemy. But he still felt unsure of himself. Just before the battle he prayed to God again.

"'Show me,' he begged, 'that I have truly been chosen to save Israel. I will put a sheepskin on the ground, and in the morning, if the fleece is soaked with the dew and the ground round about is dry, then I shall know that Thou wilt save Israel by mine hand, as Thou hast said.'

"The young man was up very early the next morning. There was the sheepskin, heavy with dew, so wet that he could wring a bowl full of water out of it. But the ground all round about was dry. So the young man believed in his heart that he was God's chosen leader."

"And did he win ? " asked Alan eagerly.

"I think we will leave that until next week," replied Mr. Richmond. "In the meantime, who was the young man ? "

CHAPTER NINETEEN

THE WARRIORS WHO LAPPED LIKE A DOG

" I KNOW who the young man was," said Margaret next Sunday evening. "His name was Gideon."

"But we still want to know if he won his fight against the Midianites," added Alan. "Go on with the story, Dad."

"Yes, he won the battle," said Mr. Richmond. "But first of all he had to pick his men. Thousands upon thousands of the Israelites gathered round Gideon on Mount Gilead. Not very far away, they could see the camp of the Midianites in the valley. The enemy had a huge army. The Bible says they covered the valley like grasshoppers, 'and their camels were without number, as the sand by the sea side.'"

"Gideon would need a big army, too," said Alan.

"That was what he thought," said Mr. Richmond. "But God told him to reduce his forces. Thirty-two thousand men of Israel had come at Gideon's summons, but first of all God told him to send away any who were afraid. Cowards are of no use in an army. And twenty-two thousand men went away when he made the proclamation. That left ten thousand.

"Then God said to Gideon : ' There are still too many. Bring them down to the water, and I will test them for you there.'

"So Gideon led his forces down to the side of the burn, and lined them up at the edge of the water. Then the test began. The soldiers were told to drink from the burn. Most of them went down on their knees and put their mouths to the water to drink. But a few of the soldiers remained standing, and bent down and scooped up the water in their hands, lapping it from their hands like a dog.

" ' These are your men,' God said to Gideon. ' The ones who lapped like a dog. Send the others home.' "

"The soldiers who remained standing were watchful," said Alan. "They would be ready to fight at any moment if they were suddenly attacked."

"I think you're right," agreed his father. "But Gideon was left with only a small company of men out of the original

41

thirty-two thousand. He and his soldiers prepared for battle.

"That night, when darkness fell, Gideon divided his troops into three companies. He gave each man a trumpet in one hand, and an earthen pot with a lamp inside it in the other. Then, in the darkness, they crept down on the Midianite camp.

"Suddenly, Gideon blew a loud, clear blast on his trumpet. It was the signal to attack. Every one of his men blew his trumpet and smashed his earthen pot. There was a sudden blaze of light from the lamps. And from all round about the camp came the war-cry : ' The sword of the Lord, and of Gideon ! '

"The enemy army awoke in terror. They burst out of their tents half-asleep, completely confused by the noise and the flashing lights. Each man attacked his neighbour, and then they all ran away in fear. So Gideon and his picked troops won their battle."

"That's one of the most exciting stories I've ever heard!" cried Alan. "But how many soldiers did Gideon have, Dad ? You didn't tell us that ! "

"No, you can find that out for yourself, Alan," said his father with a smile.

CHAPTER TWENTY

THE MAN IN THE TREE

"THERE'S a nest in the tree beside the gate," said Alan, "and it has four eggs in it."

"How do you know?" demanded Margaret. "Did you climb up?"

"Well, it's not very difficult once you get to the branches," said Alan. "I just peeped in.

"No wonder your clothes get torn," remarked his mother. "I hope you didn't take away any of the eggs, Alan."

"No, I just touched them," said Alan. "I think they'll be hatching out in about a week's time."

"Only if you leave them in peace," warned his father. But if you climb the tree every day to have a look, the mother bird may desert the nest."

"All right," agreed Alan. "I promise I won't go up there again; at least, not until the young ones are hatched. I'd like to have a peep at them some day."

"Well, I don't think that will do much harm," said his father, "so long as you just have a look and then leave them alone.

"There's a story in the Bible about a man who climbed a tree," Mr. Richmond continued. "I don't know if *he* tore his clothes or not! I don't think he cared, he was so eager to get up the tree. He was one of the wealthiest men in the busy city of Jericho, chief of the tax-gatherers. The Jews hated the tax-gatherers because they always demanded more money than they should, and this man was the most unpopular of the lot. Everyone despised him because of his job, and hated him for his greed.

"One day Jesus came through the city. The chief tax-gatherer was busy in his office when he saw the crowd gather in the street to see Jesus pass by. He wanted to see Jesus, too, but he was a little man, and there was a great crowd, and he could not see over their heads. So he ran before them, and climbed up into a sycamore tree and waited for Jesus to pass.

43

"Then he got the surprise of his life. Instead of passing by without noticing him, Jesus stopped, and looked up into the tree, and said to the man : ' Hurry up and come down ! To-day I'm going to stay at your house ! '

"The chief tax-gatherer nearly fell out of the tree in his excitement ! He slid down to the ground and welcomed Jesus. But the other people were angry. They murmured against Jesus and said that He had chosen to be the guest of a man who was a sinner.

"The chief tax-gatherer stood before Jesus and looked at Him. He felt very ashamed of himself, and yet, very joyful, too, because Jesus had chosen his home as His resting-place. Then he burst out : ' Behold, Lord, the half of my goods I give to the poor ; and if I have taken anything from any man by false accusation, I give him it back four times over ! '

"And Jesus rejoiced, and said : ' This day is salvation come to this house ! ' "

"That would be a happy day for Jesus," said Margaret.

"Yes," said her father, "and a wonderful day for the rich tax-gatherer. I wonder if you know who he was ? "

CHAPTER TWENTY-ONE

SECRET SERVICE

"THE school sports are to be held in three weeks' time," said Alan. "I'm going to have a shot at the hundred yards race. I raced Jim Cameron home from school on Friday and beat him just by a yard."

"You'll need to practise every day if you want to win," said his father. "Practice makes a good runner, you know. You and Jim remind me of the story in the Bible about the two boys who were in the Secret Service."

"In the what?" exclaimed Alan.

"The Secret Service," repeated his father. "You needn't look so surprised. There are plenty of grand adventure yarns in the Bible. This one is about two boys, and one of them was a fine runner.

"It was a troubled time for Israel. King David learned that his own son Absalom had roused the people against him. The king and his soldiers had to leave Jerusalem and go into hiding. Two of the priests of God wanted to go with him, but the king thought of a better plan.

"'Go back into the city,' he told them. 'I shall be over the hills at the back of Jordan with my men. When you have any news for me, send your sons with the message.'

"Absalom and his followers came into Jerusalem. He talked over his plans with his leading men. But king David's spies were listening. A message had to be sent to the king at once : 'Tell David to cross the Jordan immediately. Absalom is coming to attack him !'

"The two boys were waiting just outside the city. A slave-girl brought them the message for the king and at once they set out. But another boy had seen them, and he told Absalom. The hunt was up ! The boys doubled on their tracks and ran into a village. Where were they to hide ? They gasped out their story to a woman in a court-yard, and their luck held, for she was on David's side. The two boys clambered down a well in the court-yard, and

45

crouched at the bottom. The woman quickly spread a cloth over the top and scattered corn over it. In the darkness below the two boys waited for their pursuers. Soon they heard the shout of men's voices.

"'Where are these boys? Have you seen them?'

"'Yes,' said the woman. 'They've gone over the water!'"

Margaret clapped her hands. "What a clever answer," she said. "Yes, they were over the water all right . . . in the well!" said her father. "But the men thought she meant that they had crossed the river. They hunted everywhere, but at last they had to go back to Jerusalem and report that they had lost the boys.

"As soon as the coast was clear the boys came out of the well and made for David's camp, and delivered their message. And so the king was able to escape, and, later, to fight back."

"Who were the boys, Dad?" asked Alan.

"That's for you to find out," said Mr Richmond. "And next Sunday I'll tell you about the one who was a famous runner."

CHAPTER TWENTY-TWO

A FAMOUS RUNNER

"I'VE found out the names of the two boys who were in the king's secret service," said Alan next Sunday. "One was Ahimaaz and the other was Jonathan. But which of them was the famous runner?"

"He was Ahimaaz," said his father, "and I promised I'd tell you more about him. You remember I told you how David had to flee from his son, Absalom? He crossed the Jordan and made for the hills so that he could see his pursuers coming. Then he prepared his troops for battle. He wanted to go with them himself, but they would not allow it. So he took the salute while all the soldiers marched past him in their companies. Before his generals left, he gave them one instruction. 'Please be gentle, for my sake, with young Absalom.' For the king greatly loved his son, even though the foolish young man was plotting against him.

"Ahimaaz, the runner, went with David's army. There was a great battle in the forest, and king David's troops won the day."

"What happened to Absalom?" asked Margaret.

"He came to a terrible end," said her father. "He was riding on a mule, and, as the beast ran among the trees of the forest, Absalom's hair was caught in the branches overhead. He had long hair, and the more he struggled, the more it tangled in the branches. And one of the king's men stabbed him as he hung there, and killed him.

"One of the generals blew a trumpet to call back his troops. 'We must send word of our victory to the king,' he said. And at once Ahimaaz begged to be allowed to run with the good news. 'No, I cannot allow you to go,' said the general. 'The king's son is dead. That is not good news to carry.' And instead he sent a Negro slave. But Ahimaaz persisted. 'Do let me run after him,' he pleaded. And because he went on asking, the general at last let him go.

47

"Ahimaaz had been thinking. The Negro slave had gone over the hills, straight for David's camp. Ahimaaz ran by the valley of the Jordan, over flat country. And because of his speed as a runner, he was first.

"King David was waiting for news. Suddenly a watchman on a tower over the gate called out : 'I see a man running alone !' 'If he is alone he brings good news !' the king replied. After a bit the watchman said : 'I can recognise him by his style of running. It is Ahimaaz.'

"'A good man,' said the king. 'He will bring good news.'

"'I can see a second man running, too,' said the watchman.

"Soon Ahimaaz burst in and fell at the king's feet and told him that his troops had won. But he did not tell him about Absalom, and that was what the king wanted most to know. A few minutes later the Negro slave ran in. And he told the king that Absalom was dead.

"It was a sad day for the king. He forgot Absalom's evil ways and how he had lifted up his hand against his own father. All that he could think of was that his dear boy was dead. And as he went to his room he wept and cried : 'O my son Absalom, my son, my son, Absalom ! Would God I had died for thee, O Absalom, my son, my son !'"

Alan looked into the heart of the fire. "I'd like to read that story for myself," he said.

"I hope you will," said his father. "It is one of the greatest and saddest stories in the Old Testament. And when you read it, see if you can find out the name of the Negro."

CHAPTER TWENTY-THREE

THE RAVENS

"HAMISH MacDOUGALL, the gamekeeper, was telling me that he was over on Creagmore Island yesterday," said Margaret. "He says that ravens are nesting there. There are four young ones, and the mother and father birds were teaching the young ravens to fly."

"Yes, and he shot two of them," added Alan. "He told me so this morning."

"Oh, what a shame!" cried Margaret. "Why did he do that? What harm were the ravens doing?"

"Hamish says that they trouble the sheep," said Alan. "Not the healthy ones, running about, but those that fall down and can't get up again. Sometimes a sheep falls on its back and can't rise because of the weight of its wool. Then the raven swoops down and picks out its eyes. Hamish says that several of the ewes this year have been blinded by the ravens. He keeps them and their lambs in a corner of the field beside his cottage so that he can look after them."

"So you see, Margaret, why the gamekeeper has to hunt the ravens," said Mr. Richmond.

"I suppose so," said Margaret slowly. "I'm so sorry for the poor blinded sheep. I didn't know that ravens were such cruel birds."

"They're not cruel," said her father. "But they are birds of prey, like many other birds. And they have their place in nature. We read about them in the Bible. In fact, the very first bird mentioned in the whole Bible is the raven. You remember, Noah sent out a raven from the ark so that he might find out if the flood waters were going down. And the raven went to and fro in the sky until at last it found dry land on which to settle. And there is a story in the Old Testament of how God sent the ravens to keep a starving man alive."

"Tell us that story," said Margaret. "It sounds as if ravens can do some good after all."

49

"For a long, long time there had been no rain," Mr. Richmond went on, "and there was a great famine in the land. God's servant, the prophet, heard God telling him to go and live beside a stream called Cherith. And God promised that the birds would feed him. So the prophet did as he was told, and came to the side of the stream. Day by day, he had fresh water to drink. And every morning and every evening the ravens brought him food—bread and meat. So he was able to keep alive, even in the midst of a famine."

"The ravens are God's birds, too," said Margaret, "even though they do attack the sheep."

"Yes," said her father. "God cares for them and for us. One of the Psalms says : ' He giveth to the beast his food, and to the young ravens which cry.' "

"I wonder who the prophet was, to whom the ravens brought food," said Margaret. "Let's find out, Alan ! "

CHAPTER TWENTY-FOUR

RAIN

" ' **R**AIN, rain, go to Spain !
Don't come back here again ! ' "
chanted Margaret, as she looked out of the study window.
Outside, the rain fell in a steady downpour, blotting out the
view of the loch and the hills beyond.

"Mr. Cameron will be pleased," said Alan. "He said
the other day that all the farmers have been hoping for
rain for weeks. The ground is as hard as a stone."

"We'll need to look for a rainy Bible story to-night,"
said Mr. Richmond with a smile. "There's quite a lot about
rain in the Bible."

"I expect the Jewish farmers worried about their crops
just like Mr. Cameron," said Alan. "Did they get as much
rain as we usually do, Dad ? "

"Indeed they did not ! " replied his father. "Palestine
is a hot, dry country, and rain was always regarded as a
great blessing. It didn't rain just any day all the year
round as it can do here. The Jews spoke about ' the early
rain and the latter rain,' and their crops depended on them.
Sometimes the rain failed altogether, and the crops were
ruined. That is why the children of Israel always thought
of rain as a special blessing from God. No rain, no food.
The prophet Isaiah speaks about ' the rain that comes down
and waters the earth and makes it bring forth and bud that it
may give seed to the sower and bread to the eater.' "

"And is there a story about rain ? " asked Margaret.
"I mean, a real downpour, like to night, for instance."

"There certainly is," said her father. "You remember
I told you how a prophet was fed by the ravens ? That was
in a time of famine caused by the lack of rain. Everyone in
the country suffered. The king and his chief officer were
out scouring the land for fresh grass to save the lives of the
horses and cattle. But the whole land lay dry, and dusty
and parched. Then the word of God came to the prophet
Elijah.

"'Go to the king,' God said. 'Tell him that there is going to be rain.' And Elijah did as he was told.

"Then the prophet climbed up to the top of a mountain with his servant. There he sat down.

"'Look out towards the sea,' he said to his servant. The man did so. 'I can see nothing,' he reported.

"'Go again, seven times,' Elijah told him.

"And at the seventh time the man came back and said : 'I see a little cloud rising out of the sea. It is no bigger than a man's hand.'

"'It is rain !' said Elijah. 'A great rain ! Go and tell the king. Tell him to whip up his chariot and get home as fast as he can before the storm makes a swamp of the ground.'

"Before long the whole sky was black with clouds, and a shrieking wind brought lashing, heavy rain."

"Who was the king who ran before the rain ? " asked Alan.

"He was one of the kings of Israel," said his father. "You must search him out, and the story about the rain."

CHAPTER TWENTY-FIVE

THE SMITH

" JIM and I are going down to the smiddy to morrow evening," said Alan. "Old Bess cast a shoe when they were carting hay yesterday. I want to watch the smith fitting a new one."

"Oh, I must see that, too ! " cried Margaret. "I like visiting the smiddy. Perhaps Mr. MacNair will let us blow up the fire for him. I like watching the sparks fly when he hammers the hot iron into shape."

"Well, if you are going to the smiddy," said Mrs. Richmond, "you might take the big kitchen knife with you. It's very blunt. Ask Mr. MacNair if he will put a keen edge on it for me."

"I wonder what we should do without the smith," Mr. Richmond remarked. "There are very few village smiddies left nowadays. When I was a boy the smith was one of the most important men in the village. He could shoe a horse, mend a plough, make a gate, sharpen up your tools . . . oh, there were hundreds of jobs for the smith to do. But nowadays there are so few horses that he can barely make a living."

"I wonder if Mr. MacNair longs for the days when the smith sharpened the clansmen's swords," said Alan mischievously. "The smiddy must have been a busy place long ago when the clans were fighting. Now the smith only gets kitchen knives to sharpen ! "

"You're very blood-thirsty to-night, Alan," said his father, with a smile. "I wonder if you have heard about the time when there were no smiths in all the land of Israel? The Israelites were continually at war with the Philistines in the land of Canaan. And things were going very badly with the people of Israel. The Philistine warriors were numbered by the thousand. The Bible says that they had thirty thousand chariots, six thousand horsemen, and ordinary soldiers as numerous as the sand on the sea-shore.

And the men of Israel were afraid. They hid in caves and in the woods and among the rocks, for fear of the enemy.

"The Philistines made laws to prevent any trouble from the Israelites. They would not allow a single Jewish smith to practise his trade. There was to be no making of spears or swords. No weapons of any kind were allowed. And, if the Israelites wanted their ploughs and axes and hoes or other tools sharpened, they had to go meekly to the Philistine smiths to do the work for them."

"So they couldn't fight against their enemies?" said Margaret.

"Not just then," said her father. "But they had two leaders, the king and his son, who brought new hope to the children of Israel. And they knew that God had promised that the land of Canaan would belong to them some day."

"I must ask Mr. MacNair if he knows that story," said Alan, "about the time when there was no smith in all the land of Israel."

"You had better read the story for yourself, first," said his father. "Then you will be able to tell me the names of the two leaders, the king and his son."

CHAPTER TWENTY-SIX

A BUNCH OF GRAPES

"**W**E went through the gardens at the Castle this afternoon," said Margaret. "I've never seen anything so lovely. They have all sorts of flowers I've never even heard of, and there didn't seem to be a bare patch anywhere."

"I like the green-house best," said Alan. "Bunches and bunches of grapes, and peaches and tomatoes. Mr. MacAllister let us taste them all. They were delicious!"

"Yes, the laird has a good gardener in Mr. MacAllister," said Mr. Richmond. "The Castle gardens sound like a land flowing with milk and honey, by your description. Your mother and I must walk up there some day and see the fine show before the Summer is over."

"Where was the real land flowing with milk and honey, Daddy?" asked Margaret. "I'm sure that's a saying from the Bible."

"Yes, it is," replied her father. "The children of Israel were always talking about it. You see, they had been wandering year after year in the hot, dusty desert. Day after day, there was sand, and rocks, and little else. But their leaders always kept them going by telling them that they were journeying to a land flowing with milk and honey. The words became a kind of watchword to them. Milk and honey meant abundance of everything, trees laden with fruit, clear springs of water, fruitful fields, and cattle on all the hills, bees busy among the flowers, and everything that was lovely."

"And did they find their land flowing with milk and honey?" asked Alan.

"Yes, they did," said his father. "But like all things worth having, they had to strive for it. You were talking about grapes, Alan. Well, this is a story about a bunch of grapes. And it is a spy story, too."

"The Mystery of the Bunch of Grapes!" said Margaret. "That's a thrilling name for it!"

"The Israelites came to the borders of the rich land,"
Mr. Richmond went on. "But they wanted to find out more
about it. So Moses chose twelve spies, one from each of the
tribes of Israel. You will find the names of the twelve men
written down in the Bible.

"'Go and see what kind of land it is,' he commanded,
'and bring us back word.'

"So the spies went off, and travelled stealthily through
the strange land, noting how the people lived, looking at
the crops, and the woodlands and the vineyards. And, in
a valley, by the side of a stream, they found bunches of
grapes hanging heavy from the vines. So they cut down a
branch with a cluster of grapes on it. It was so heavy that
it had to be slung on a stick and carried on the shoulders of
two men. Then they went back to the Jewish camp. They
didn't need to say much. What they had brought in their
hands spoke louder than words.

"'We came into the land to which you sent us,' they
reported, 'and surely it flows with milk and honey, and this
is the fruit of it.'"

"I wonder what they called that fine country," said
Alan.

"Well, I leave you to find that out," said his father.

CHAPTER TWENTY-SEVEN

THE CUNNING FOX

"I SAW a fox yesterday," announced Alan importantly. Jim Cameron and I were fishing up the hill, and the fox ran quite close to us. Jim says it must live up among the rocks at the head of the burn. His mother has lost several chickens recently, and Mr. Cameron is sure that the fox has taken them. He says he's going to sit up one night with a gun and wait for the rascal."

"They're not so easy to kill," remarked his father. "The fox is a very cunning beast, and if he thinks there is danger, well, he just won't be there. Even the Bible hasn't a very good word to say for the fox. They were cunning, thieving beasts in those days, just as they often are to-day."

"Did they steal chickens ? " asked Margaret.

"Yes, and anything else they could get," said her father. "But what annoyed the farmers most was the way they spoiled the grapes."

"Grapes ! " cried Margaret. "How lovely ! You had them when you were ill last winter, Mummy. Don't you remember ? "

"Yes, and I remember a little fox called Margaret who used to come in and see me and eat them up ! " smiled her mother.

"But I didn't *steal* them ! " protested Margaret. "I just asked you for a few."

"Well, the foxes in the Bible weren't content with a few," said her father. "No sooner did the grapes ripen than the foxes were in among them, and they did a great deal of damage. Solomon, who wrote the long poem called ' The Song of Solomon,' said : ' Let us catch the foxes, the little foxes, that spoil the vines : for our vines have tender grapes.'

"Jesus called a man a fox once," Mr. Richmond went on. "It was a brave thing to do, for the man was Governor of the land where Jesus lived. He was a crafty, deceitful man, and a wicked man, too. He had killed Jesus' cousin, John the Baptist, because John had warned him about his evil life. Then he heard about Jesus, of how He went about preaching and teaching and doing good. At first he got a fright. He thought it was John come to life again. Then he thought of a crafty plan to get Jesus out of his country.

"'I'll frighten Him,' he said to himself, 'and then He'll run away and leave me in peace.'

"So he sent men to Jesus to threaten Him. 'Get out of this country. If you don't, the ruler will kill you.' But Jesus wasn't afraid. 'Go and tell that fox,' He said, 'that you found me casting out evil spirits and healing the sick.'"

"Jesus knew that the ruler was just trying to frighten Him," said Alan wisely. "No wonder He called him a fox."

"Yes, but I think there's more in the story than that," said Mr. Richmond. "You see, the ruler wanted Jesus to do what he said. But Jesus lived by what God said. And that is always the right thing to do."

"I wonder who the fox was," said Alan thoughtfully.

"I'll give you one hint," said his father. "The story is told by St. Luke."

CHAPTER TWENTY-EIGHT

TWO SMALL FISHES

"JIM and I had a wonderful day, yesterday," said Alan. "We tramped for miles and miles up into the hills, following the burn. Jim says there's a trout in every pool. The burn got smaller and smaller, until it was just a tiny trickle that we could jump over. And we had to keep out of sight, in case the fish should see us."

"The trout must have got smaller and smaller, too," said Margaret mischievously. "At least, the two you brought home were very tiny!"

"The water was too clear," said Alan. "And the sun was too bright. We need a day or two of heavy rain to put the burn in spate. That's the best time for fishing! A dull day, and plenty of water in the burn. Then I'll bring home enough trout to feed all of you."

"You are like the boy in the Bible, Alan," said Mr. Richmond. "But he did more than feed a family. He helped to feed five thousand people!

"I don't know whether he had been fishing that morning or not," Mr. Richmond went on. "But the Bible certainly says that he was carrying five barley loaves and two small fishes."

Margaret smiled. "Just like you, Alan," she said. "Two *small* fishes!"

"The boy found himself with a great crowd of people," Mr. Richmond continued. "They were looking for Jesus, because He had done so many miracles of healing. So the boy went along with them too, just to see what would happen."

"Did they find Jesus?" asked Margaret.

"Yes, He was high up, on top of a mountain, talking to His disciples," said her father. "When He looked up, there was the crowd, thousands of folk, toiling up the steep hillside towards Him."

"They must have been very tired," said Alan.

"Tired and hungry," agreed his father. "They had come a long way. That was the first thing Jesus thought of.

He felt sorry for them all. So He said to Philip : ' Where are we going to buy enough bread to feed them all ? '

"Philip was dismayed. ' Two-hundred pennyworth of bread would not be enough, even to give each of them a little,' he said.

"But another of the disciples had noticed the boy. He put his hand on his shoulder and led him through the crowd to Jesus. ' Master ! ' he said. ' Here is a boy with something to eat. He has five barley loaves and two small fishes. But what use are they among so many ? '

"Jesus looked round upon the crowd. ' Make them all sit down,' He told His disciples. So they all sat down, five thousand of them, on the green, grassy slopes of the mountain. Then Jesus took the loaves and the fishes and gave thanks to God. He broke the boy's gift into pieces and shared them among His disciples. They took the bread and fish round the people. And there was enough for everyone to eat."

"That was a miracle picnic," said Margaret.

Her father nodded his head. "Yes," he said. "A miracle from a boy's gift."

"The boy must have been very proud that day," said Alan, "because he was able to help Jesus. Do you know his name, Dad ? "

Mr. Richmond shook his head. "No, but I know the name of the disciple who brought him to Jesus," he said. "Do you ? "

CHAPTER TWENTY-NINE

CATERPILLARS

"THE gooseberries are almost ready," said Mrs. Richmond one Sunday night. "We must all have an evening in the garden some day after you two come home from school. I want to make some jelly, and perhaps we'll have a gooseberry tart. There seems to be a good crop this year."

"They're good gooseberries, too," said Alan. "Especially the big red ones."

"You're giving yourself away, Alan," said his father, with a twinkle in his eye. "We were blaming the birds for eating them, but it seems that some big ' birds ' have been helping themselves, too ! "

"I've just had a few," Alan admitted. "They are scrumptious when you eat them straight from the bush, ripe and warm in the sun."

"I like them best in a gooseberry tart," said Margaret. "There are nasty, hairy caterpillars on the bushes, and I'm always afraid that I'll pick one of them in mistake for a gooseberry."

They all laughed.

"That wouldn't taste so nice," agreed her father. "The caterpillars are a nuisance. Nothing seems to stop them, and they like the gooseberry bushes better than anything else in the garden."

"Do you know of any gooseberries in the Bible, Daddy?" asked Margaret.

"No," said Mr. Richmond. "I don't think you'll find that fruit in the Bible. But there are plenty of caterpillars. One of the most famous kings of Israel mentioned them in a prayer to God.

"It was during a time of great rejoicing among the Jews," Mr. Richmond went on. "For many long years the children of Israel had wanted to build a Temple for the worship of the one true God. King David had planned to build it, but his reign was greatly troubled, and he did not fulfil his dream. But his son completed the work when he

61

became king. He built the finest Temple the people could ever have imagined, of the most beautiful and costly materials. Everyone gave something to help in the building and furnishing, and everything was of the best, for it was God's house. At last the Temple was completed, and the king called all the people together.

"A great crowd gathered all round the Temple while the king went in to pray. He gave thanks to God for all that He had done for the nation since the days when He had led them out of Egypt. And he asked God to continue to be with them, and guide them.

"'When the people come to pray in this holy place,' he said, 'hear thou in heaven thy dwelling place : and when thou hearest, forgive.'

"Then he asked God to keep them free from all evil, from famine and pestilence, from locusts and from caterpillars, from fear of their enemies and from plague and sickness. You see, he knew that the caterpillars and the locusts could eat up all their crops and thus bring famine and hunger throughout the land. So the king asked God's protection against them."

"I know what you are going to ask now, Daddy," said Margaret. "Who was the king who prayed about the caterpillars ? "

"Quite right, Margaret," said her father. "And I hope you will read the whole of his prayer to God for the good of the people he ruled over."

CHAPTER THIRTY

THE BATHING POOL (I)

"WE'VE found a wonderful bathing place at the mouth of the burn," said Margaret. "There's a big pool, with sand at the bottom, deep enough for swimming. We splashed in and out all afternoon, yesterday, it was so hot."

"Jim and I are going to rig up a plank with one end over the pool," Alan chimed in. "Then we can practise diving."

"Your own private swimming pool, in fact!" said Mr. Richmond with a smile. "'Better than all the waters of Israel!'"

"Our Bible story!" cried Margaret. "Is it about a bathing pool, Daddy?"

"It is," said her father. "A pool in the river Jordan, just like your pool in the Lussa.

"The story really begins with a kidnapped girl," Mr. Richmond went on. "A Jewish girl, probably just a little bit older than you, Margaret. One day a troop of Syrian warriors swept through her village. There was no time to run. One of the horsemen stooped down from his saddle and caught her up beside him as his horse raced on.

"'This will please my master, the Captain,' he said to himself. 'I shall give him the girl as a slave for his wife.'

"And so it was. The little Jewish girl lived in the house of the Captain, and waited on his wife."

"Poor little girl!" said Margaret. "She must have felt very sad, so far from home."

"I'm sure she did," agreed her father. "But there was sadness in the Captain's house, too, and the little girl soon noticed it. The Syrian Captain was a great man and a good man, and he was a famous warrior. But he was a leper, and the horror of that terrible disease hung over the house like a dark shadow.

"The Jewish maid forgot her own sorrows in her pity for the Captain. One day she plucked up courage and spoke about it to her mistress.

"'Oh, if only my lord the Captain could go to the

prophet who is in Samaria!' she said. 'He would be able to heal him of his leprosy!'

"It seemed almost too good to be true," Mr. Richmond went on. "If all the wise doctors in Syria were helpless, what could a Jewish prophet do? But the Captain's wife sent a message to her husband and told him what the little girl had said. And the words of the slave girl came to the ears of the king, too. The king thought very highly of his Captain, and he acted at once.

"'I will write a letter to the king of Israel,' he said. 'He will do anything that I ask. You must go to Samaria immediately.'

"So the Captain set out in his chariot with new hope in his heart. Behind him were his soldiers, carrying rich gifts for the king of Israel. They stopped only for brief rests, then sped on across the desert. Perhaps at last the Captain was going to be cured of his terrible disease."

"What an exciting story!" Alan burst out. "I can almost see the horses galloping across the desert!"

"Was the Captain cured?" asked Margaret. "That's what I want to know!"

Mr. Richmond looked at the clock.

"Bed-time!" he said firmly. "We'll have the rest of the story next week, just like a serial story. But I expect that you will have found out the Captain's name before then."

CHAPTER THIRTY-ONE

THE BATHING POOL (II)

"WELL, where were we?" said Mr. Richmond, next Sunday evening. "I know that we haven't reached the bathing pool yet!"

"The Syrian soldiers were galloping across the desert," said Alan promptly. "And the Captain's name was Naaman. We found him in the Second Book of Kings."

"I'm sorry that the Bible doesn't tell us the name of the little girl," said Margaret. "But for her, Captain Naaman would never even have heard of the prophet in Samaria."

Mr. Richmond nodded. "The Bible is full of nameless folk like the Jewish maid," he said. "But they are God's servants, just the same. The little girl repaid good for evil when she told her mistress about the prophet who could heal Captain Naaman.

"The Syrian horsemen came into the land of Israel," Mr. Richmond went on. "Captain Naaman went straight to the king of Israel and gave him the letter from the Syrian king. When the king of Israel read it, he was sorely troubled. 'Syria is trying to pick a quarrel with me!' he cried. 'How can I cure a man of his leprosy? Am I God, to kill and to make alive?'

"But the prophet in Samaria heard of the king's dismay. 'Send the stranger Captain to me,' he said.

"So Naaman came proudly with his chariot and his horsemen to the door of the prophet's humble home. But no one made a fuss over his arrival, great man though he was in his own land. Only a servant was sent out with a simple message from the man of God: 'Go and wash in Jordan seven times, and thy flesh shall come again to thee, and thou shalt be clean.'

"Captain Naaman was angry. First of all, the prophet had not come out to greet his important visitor. Now there was this message. Why bathe in the wretched little

Jordan stream ? Were not Abana and Pharpar, the rivers of his own land, better than all the waters of Israel ? Could he not wash in them and be clean ?

"So the Captain strode back to his chariot in a rage. He prepared to turn homewards again, across the dusty desert. And he was still a leper.

"But one of his soldiers, greatly daring, came to the chariot. He looked up into his Captain's dark, angry face. ' Sir,' he said, ' if the prophet had told you to do some great thing, would you not have done it ? How simple, then, it is when he says only : ' Wash and be clean '.'

"The scowl cleared from Naaman's brow. Without a word he got down from his chariot and went down into the valley of the Jordan. In a deep pool of cool, clear water he bathed himself seven times. And when he came out of the water the seventh time, his skin was whole and firm and clean again, like the skin of a little child.

"Then Captain Naaman and all his company came and stood before the prophet.

" ' Now I know that there is no God in all the earth but in Israel,' he said humbly."

"He must have felt very excited on his way home," said Alan. "Now I shall always remember the Captain when we bathe in our pool."

"And the man of God ? " asked Mr. Richmond. "I expect you know who he was, don't you ? "

CHAPTER THIRTY-TWO

DUSTY FEET

MARGARET took off her sandals and wiggled her toes. Sand from her bare feet fell like golden dust on the floor.

"It's easy to see that you have been down at the beach, to-day," said Mrs. Richmond. "But you should have remembered to shake the sand out of your shoes before you came into the house."

"My shoes are full of sand, too," added Alan. "And my feet are very tired and hot. I tried to walk home barefoot, but the small stones on the road hurt too much. Jim Cameron laughs at me. He says my feet are soft because I wore shoes in Glasgow. His are as tough as leather. During the holidays he runs about barefoot all the time, except on Sundays."

"Just like the boys and girls of the Bible," remarked Mr. Richmond. "I don't suppose they ever wore anything on their feet. Even the grown-ups wore only a simple kind of sandal. Every now and then they would stop, and take off their sandals to knock the dust and sand off their feet."

"But not indoors!" said Mrs. Richmond, with a smile.

"No," Mr. Richmond agreed. "When they came into the house there was usually a basin of cool, clean water waiting to wash away all the dust and weariness of the journey. That was one of the first courtesies one paid to a visitor . . . to wash the dust from his tired feet.

"One of the most beautiful stories in the Gospels is the story of Jesus washing His disciples' feet. It happened after supper, the Last Supper, in the upper room in Jerusalem. Jesus rose quietly from the table and tied a towel about Him. Then He poured water into a basin and knelt at the feet of each of His disciples. One by one, He washed their feet and dried them with the towel.

"One of the disciples was very much ashamed that Jesus should kneel before him.

"'Thou shalt never wash my feet!' he protested.

"But Jesus explained to them all why He was doing

67

this. 'Ye call me Master and Lord,' He said. 'And ye say well; for so I am. If I, then, your Lord and Master, have washed your feet; ye also ought to wash one another's feet. For I have given you an example, that ye should do as I have done to you.'"

"And did that disciple allow Jesus to wash his feet?" asked Margaret.

"He did," said Mr. Richmond. "I wonder if you know which of the twelve it was?"

"Why did Jesus say that He was giving them an example?" asked Alan. "We don't wash one another's feet nowadays."

"It was His way of teaching them the meaning of loving and humble service," said his father. "And Jesus taught His disciples a new commandment that night, too, to make sure that they really understood His action. He said to them: 'My new commandment is this: that ye love one another, as I have loved you.'"

CHAPTER THIRTY-THREE

THE GIFTS THAT BUILT A CHURCH

NEXT Sunday we've all to take a gift to the Sunday School," said Margaret one night.

"A gift? What for?" asked her mother.

"Well, it's a kind of thanksgiving service," explained Alan. "We're trying to collect all kinds of things, food, and books, and old toys, to send to the sick children in the County Hospital."

"As a thanksgiving to God because we are well and strong," added Margaret.

"What are you going to give, Margaret?" asked her mother.

"Oh, I think I'll take one of my dolls and some of my picture-books. I'm sure some little sick girl will enjoy having them."

"And I'm going to take six fresh eggs," Alan put in. He had recently bought two hens with his pocket money and he was very proud of his success as a poultry farmer.

"Your gift service reminds me of a story in the Old Testament," said Mr. Richmond. "It is about offerings that the people of Israel brought to God when they were wandering in the wilderness. God spoke to Moses and told him to build a tabernacle, or church, for His worship. He described very carefully how His house was to be built. Then Moses called the people together and told them what God had said. Everyone was to have a share in it, and it was to be a willing offering.

"'Whosoever is of a willing heart, let him bring it, an offering unto the Lord,' said Moses.

"So the people brought their gifts. Gold, and silver, and brass, and precious stones, and leather and linen and timber. They brought everything that was needed for the work, and everything was of the best. In fact, they brought too much, and Moses had to tell them to stop."

"Where did they get the gold and silver and brass to bring?" asked Alan.

"They gave Moses their ear-rings and rings and bracelets and other ornaments," said his father. "And the men and women wove fine linen and cloth. Two skilled workmen were chosen for the work, and they melted down the ornaments to make the candlesticks and dishes and lamps for the holy place. But I think the most interesting thing of all was the wash-basin."

"A wash-basin in church!" exclaimed Margaret.

"Yes," said her father. "Whenever the priests went in to lead the worship, they had to wash their feet and their hands from the dust and sand of the desert, so that they came before God cleansed and holy. Do you know what that wash-basin was made from? It was made of the mirrors that the women brought. Mirrors of polished brass, for there were no glass mirrors in those days. The women's mirrors were all put in the furnace and melted down to make a beautiful wash-basin, or laver, as the Bible calls it, of solid brass.

"I wonder if you can find out the names of the two skilled workmen who were chosen to adorn the tabernacle from the gifts that the people brought? And I hope that you, when you take your gifts to the Sunday School next week, will be 'willing-hearted,' like the Israelites. The Bible says: 'God loveth a cheerful giver.'"

CHAPTER THIRTY-FOUR

THE WELL OF MEMORY

"I MET such a strange old man this afternoon," said Margaret one Sunday night. "It was up near the old ruins. I was going to take the flowers from the Sunday School to Mrs. MacVicar, because she has been ill. And I found the old man sitting on a stone beside the well."

"What was he doing there ? " asked Alan.

"I'm not quite sure," said Margaret slowly. "I said ' Good-afternoon ' to him, and he smiled and took off his hat. He told me he'd come all the way from Canada."

"A Canadian ! " exclaimed Alan. "Did he speak with a funny accent ? "

"Oh, no, he wasn't a Canadian. He'd lived in Canada since he was a young man. But he was born here, in Craig-lussach, and his voice was Highland. He told me that he had been born in the cottage which is all broken down, and that he'd come back to see it. And he drank some of the cold well water and said it was the finest water in all the world. He said he'd often wearied for a drink of it when he was far from home."

"Just like the king in the Bible," said Mr. Richmond.

"Another story ! " said Alan. "Who was the king, Daddy ? "

"I'll let you find that out," said his father. "It won't be very hard to guess, this time.

"The king was like your friend of this afternoon, Margaret. He was far from his boyhood home. He was in trouble, too. His enemies were searching for him, and they were very powerful. In fact, if he hadn't been encouraged by his bodyguard of soldiers, I think the king would have lost heart altogether. The enemy had captured Bethlehem, the village where he was born, and the king was hiding in a cave in the mountains. It was very hot. In the valley below, the king could see the people gathering in the harvest. He remembered his home, and thought longingly of the well there . . . the finest water in all the world, as your friend said, Margaret. But his home, and the well, were in the hands of the enemy.

"The king sighed. 'Oh, if someone would only give me a drink from the well at Bethlehem, the well beside the gate!' he said. He didn't know that anyone was listening. But three of his captains, the bravest of the brave, had heard him. They went down the hill-side and made their way to Bethlehem. More than once they had to fight for it, but they kept on. And at the risk of their lives they drew some water from the well at the gate of Bethlehem and brought it in triumph back to the king."

"How glad the king must have been!" said Margaret. "He must have enjoyed that drink of water from his own home."

"He didn't drink it," said Mr. Richmond. "He poured it out on the ground as an offering to God.

"'I could never drink such precious water,' he said. 'It was brought at the risk of men's lives!'"

"I wonder if the old man from Canada knew that story," said Margaret.

"I expect he did," said her father. "Everyone loves his own home best of all, and your friend came a long way for his precious drink of water. And I expect he thanked God, too, this afternoon, for bringing him safely home after all these years."

CHAPTER THIRTY-FIVE

MOTHS

"HOW the days are drawing in ! " said Mrs. Richmond one Sunday night. "It's getting quite dark already, though it is only eight o'clock. A few weeks ago it was quite bright until eleven."

"I'd better light the lamp," said Mr. Richmond. "But we won't draw the curtains yet. It's a pity to shut out the last of an Autumn day."

He rose and busied himself with the big, old-fashioned oil lamp. Soon a soft glow of light filled the room.

"There we are ! " said Mr. Richmond, as he settled himself in his chair again. "Now, what about our Bible story for to-night ? "

As he spoke, there was a fluttering sound. Something large and dark darted round and round the lamp for a moment, casting black shadows on the wall.

"Oh ! " cried Margaret. "What's that ? It gave me quite a fright. It must be a bird which has come in through the window."

"Or a bat," suggested Alan, as he jumped to his feet. "Bats don't see well in the light, and it may have been dazzled by the lamp."

They all looked round the room, but their mysterious visitor seemed to have disappeared.

"Oho ! " cried Mr. Richmond all at once. "There's the rascal who gave us all a fright ! " He pointed to a dark corner of the ceiling. There, quite still, with its wings spread out, was a big moth.

"What a monster one ! " cried Alan. "Shall I catch it, Dad ? "

"Well, we'd better try to drive it out into the garden where it belongs," said his father. "Otherwise it will flutter into the flames of the lamp and singe its wings."

So Margaret opened the window as wide as it would go, and Alan balanced himself on the arm of a chair and flicked his handkerchief at the moth. At once it darted away, swooped again round the lamp, and then flew out of the window into the garden.

"That's that!" said Mrs. Richmond as she helped Margaret to close the window. "I don't want any moths inside the house. I know how much damage they can do! Remember when we were packing all our clothes to come to Craiglussach? Some of the things that had been lying in a drawer for a long, long time were badly eaten away by moths."

"But not big garden moths," said Alan. "They must have been the wee, wee moths that hide in cupboards and drawers."

"Well, big moths or wee moths, I think they are better outside!" said Mrs. Richmond decidedly. "The clothes moths seem to get into the house no matter what I do, and they enjoy eating our best clothes."

"We had a text about moths in the Sunday School not long ago," said Margaret. "Jesus said: 'Lay not up for yourselves treasures upon earth, where moth and rust doth corrupt, and where thieves break through and steal. But lay up for yourselves treasures in heaven, where neither moth nor rust doth corrupt, and where thieves do not break through nor steal.' I suppose the moths are really thieves, breaking through and stealing our clothes!"

"Well, the moth has given you your Bible story for to-night," said Mr. Richmond, with a smile. "But there is another verse in the Bible where someone speaks of 'a garment that is moth eaten.' Do you know who said that?"

CHAPTER THIRTY-SIX

COCK-CROW

"HAVE you shut up your hens for the night, Alan?" asked his mother. "The hen-house door must have been loose last night, for they were all wandering about the garden early this morning."

"Yes, Mum, they're all in safe and sound," Alan replied. "I'm sorry about last night. I can't have tied up the door properly."

"The cockerel certainly made plenty of noise!" said Mr. Richmond with a smile. "He was strutting up and down outside my window at dawn this morning, crowing for all he was worth!"

"He was saying: 'Time to get UP! Time to get UP!'" said Mrs. Richmond. "But I don't think either of you two sleepy-heads heard him at all!"

Margaret grinned. "Just like the alarm clock," she said. "I never hear it either!"

"The cock was a kind of New Testament alarm clock," remarked Mr. Richmond. "It was a signal to the Roman soldiers who were on duty that one watch was ending and another beginning. And the crowing of a cock comes into the story of Jesus, one of the saddest parts of the story.

"Just after the Last Supper, Jesus and His disciples went out of the city to the peaceful hill-side. Jesus was very sorrowful. He told His companions that they would all run away and leave Him soon. The disciples protested.

"'Never!' said one of them. 'Even though I should die with you, yet will I not deny you!'

"Jesus shook His head sadly. 'Truly, I tell you,' He said, 'this very night, before cock-crow, you shall deny me three times!'

"That night Jesus' enemies came out to arrest Him, and, as He had foretold, all His disciples ran away and left Him. But the one who had spoken so strongly followed the crowd a long way off, to see what was going to happen. He slipped into the courtyard of the high priest's palace, among the servants. It was still dark, and he hoped he wouldn't be noticed.

"After a time, a servant girl saw him. She stopped and spoke. 'You were with Jesus of Galilee!' she said accusingly. The disciple was very frightened.

"'I don't know what you are talking about!' he cried roughly. And he moved hastily away.

"But another girl caught sight of his face in the moonlight and said to some of the servants: 'This fellow was also with Jesus of Nazareth.'

"Again he denied it. 'I don't know the man!' he swore. But they crowded round him. 'Surely you are one of His followers?' they said, 'for you are a Galilean. Your accent gives you away!'

"By now the disciple was thoroughly frightened. He, too, might be caught and killed. He began to curse and to swear, protesting loudly that he didn't know Jesus at all.

"Then, suddenly, the cock crowed loud and clear, at the dawning of a new day. The man remembered what Jesus had said. And he ran off, weeping bitterly. He had, in truth, denied his Lord."

"Poor disciple," said Margaret. "I'm sure we would all have been frightened, too."

Mr. Richmond nodded. "Yes," he said, "there are times when we all deny Jesus in the company of other people. But Jesus gave that disciple another chance, when He came to him after He had risen again. And the man did not fail Him then. Do you know who he was?"

CHAPTER THIRTY-SEVEN

HOME WEAVING

"I WENT to see Mrs. MacVicar again, yesterday," said
Margaret. "Do you know what she was doing?
She was weaving cloth!"

"What kind of cloth?" asked Alan.

"Tweed for a jacket," replied his sister. "She said
she hopes to send it to the Highland Show at Oban next
month, and maybe it will win a prize."

Mr. Richmond smiled. "I wonder if she told you that
she has won a prize every year for the last ten years?" he
said. "Mrs. MacVicar's tweed is famous all over Argyll.
People say it wears forever."

"Then you'd better order some to make a suit for
Alan," Mrs. Richmond broke in. "He has worn and torn all
his clothes on his fishing expeditions."

"What colour of cloth does she make?" asked Alan.

"Oh, that's the most interesting part," said Margaret.
"She had a big pot on the fire when I was there, and in it
were roots and berries boiling and bubbling to make the
dye for the cloth."

"She sounds like an old witch!" said Alan mischievously. "Stirring, and muttering her charms over a big,
black pot."

"Indeed, you're far wrong there, Alan," said his father.
"Mrs. MacVicar is one of the finest old ladies I've ever met.
She's a saint of God, always looking for ways to help folk.
She doesn't remind *me* of a witch. She reminds me of a lady
in the Bible who was very like her in some ways.

"This lady was famous for her dyes, just like Mrs.
MacVicar. She sold purple cloth, the colour that kings wear,
in the town where she lived. The purple colour was got from
shell-fish which were gathered along the coast, just like the
mussels you gather for bait, Alan.

"The seller of purple, as the people called her, was a
good woman. She used to go down to the riverside on a
Sabbath where the Jews went to worship God. And one

77

day, on the bank of the river, she heard a man preaching, a stranger to the town. She heard him talk about Jesus the Saviour, the Son of God. And, as she listened, God touched her heart, and she believed, and was baptised in the waters of the river. She brought her family to be baptised, too, so that they could share in the new joy that she had found."

"Where was the town?" asked Alan.

"It was a city called Philippi," said his father. "I think this lady was the very first Christian in all Europe. She wondered what she could do for Jesus. Then she decided that whenever these Christian preachers came to Philippi, they must stay at her house. And so that became her work for Jesus. There was always a welcome at her home, whenever they arrived, foot-sore or weary or discouraged. It was the first Christian home in Europe."

"I wonder who she was?" mused Margaret. "How strange it is to think of a lady like Mrs. MacVicar in the Bible!"

"Well, you must find out her name for yourself," said Mr. Richmond. "And what about the preacher who told her about Jesus? Who was he?"

CHAPTER THIRTY-EIGHT

THE GOLDEN MICE

"LOOK! There's a mouse!" cried Margaret suddenly. Everyone jumped up.

"Too late," said Alan. "We've frightened it off. It has gone behind the book-case."

"I must remember to get a mouse-trap to-morrow," said Mrs. Richmond. "There's probably a nest of mice in the wall, and I don't like them about the house."

"There are dozens and dozens of them in Mr. Cameron's barn," Alan broke in. "He says there seems to be a plague of them this year. I've seen them in the fields, too, when the corn was being cut."

"That reminds me of a story in the Bible," said Mr. Richmond.

"What about?" asked Margaret. "About the harvest, or about mice?"

"Both!" replied her father. "It's another story about the fighting days of the children of Israel. They were at war with the Philistines, and to encourage them in battle, the Israelites took with them their most treasured possession, the Ark of the Covenant. At first the Philistines were afraid when they heard of it.

"'God is come into the camp of Israel,' they said. 'How can we fight against God?'

"The battle began. It went very badly for the Israelites. They were put to flight, and many were killed. But, worst of all, the Philistines captured the Ark of the Covenant. They took it in triumph to their cities. But wherever the Ark of the Lord came, it brought disaster to the Philistines. Plague spread all over the country, and the people cried out in terror and pain.

"The Ark was with the Philistines for seven months, and it seemed to bring them nothing but trouble and disease. At last they asked their wise men what to do.

"'Send it away,' was their advice. 'Send it back to

79

the Israelites. It is the Ark of their God, and we have done wrong in taking it.'

"So the Philistines made a new cart and yoked to it two young cows. On the cart they laid the Ark. And in a box beside the Ark they put an offering to God, as a sign of their repentance. Now, what do you think the offering was?"

"Jewels?" said Margaret. "Corn and fruit?" suggested Alan.

Mr. Richmond shook his head.

"Mice!" he said. "Five mice made of gold. They were a symbol of the plague that had troubled the Philistines.

"The cows made their way along the country road, lowing as they went, until they came into the land of the Israelites. Some of the villagers were busy in the harvest field, reaping the wheat, when they heard the lowing of the cattle and the rumble of cart wheels. Then they saw the Ark of the Covenant, and their hearts were full of joy. The cart came to a stop in a field where there was a great stone. The Israelites broke up the wooden cart to make a fire, and sacrificed to God there and then, in thanksgiving for the return of the Ark."

"Why were there *five* golden mice, Dad?" asked Alan.

"One for each of the five great cities of the Philistines," said his father. "Now, I wonder if you can discover whose field it was to which the Ark of the Lord came home?"

CHAPTER THIRTY-NINE

THE FRUIT TREE

"THE plums will be ready in another week," said Margaret as she drew the curtains one Sunday night. "They're growing thick along the wall. I wonder why that old plum tree at the bottom of the garden grows so much better than all the others ? It's absolutely covered with plums ! "

"I know why," said Alan. "It's because of the burn on the other side of the wall. The roots of the tree go right underneath the wall, into the burn."

"Quite right, Alan ! " agreed his father. "The dry weather never worries that old tree. Its roots go right down into the life-giving water. No wonder the plums are so big and juicy ! "

"It's like the good man in the first Psalm," Margaret broke in.

> " ' He shall be like a tree that grows
> Near planted by a river,
> Which in his season yields his fruit,
> And his leaf fadeth never.' "

Mr. Richmond chuckled. "You're making up your own Bible story to-night," he said. "But I was thinking of another good man in the Bible who is likened to a tree, or, rather, to the bough of a fruit tree."

"Who was he ? " asked Margaret. "Tell us about him, Dad, and let's see if we know him."

"His life was what we call ' a success story '," said Mr. Richmond. " ' From shepherd boy to Prime Minister '."

Alan frowned thoughtfully. "I don't remember any Prime Minister in the Bible," he said.

"Well, he was," said his father. "Prime Minister of one of the greatest kingdoms in the world.

"As a boy, he was one of a large family, the second youngest, and his brothers didn't like him because he was his father's favourite. In fact, I'm afraid he was a little bit spoiled. But that doesn't excuse what his brothers did. They sold him as a slave, and he was carried away to a foreign land. Then they went home and told their father that his favourite had been eaten by wild beasts."

"Poor boy!" said Margaret. "He would feel very lonely, so far from home."

"I'm sure he did," said her father. "But he worked hard, and had many adventures, and by and by he came to be the king's right hand man.

"It came about in a strange way. He foretold that there was going to be a long time of rich crops in the land, followed by a long time of famine. Because of his wisdom, the king made him ruler over all the land. During the years of plenty, the Prime Minister gathered corn in great store-houses. Then, when the hungry days came, there were rations for all. People came from far away to buy food. Among them came the brothers who had treated the Prime Minister so badly when he was a shepherd boy. They didn't recognise him in his splendour. But he knew them. And instead of taking his revenge, he gave them corn and welcomed them to his home. And before long, he brought his father and all the family to live with him."

"His father must have been very happy," said Margaret.

"Yes," said Mr. Richmond. "When he was an old, old man he gave his sons his blessing. And, as he laid his hands on the head of the Prime Minister, his favourite son, he called him: 'a fruitful bough, even a fruitful bough by a well, whose branches run over the wall.'"

"Just like our plum tree," said Alan.

"Yes," agreed his father. "And who was the Prime Minister?"

CHAPTER FORTY

BRAMBLES

"OH dear ! " sighed Mrs. Richmond. "I don't know how I'm going to get my hands clean. I've scrubbed and scrubbed, but they're still stained with the juice of those brambles we gathered yesterday ! "

"And my jacket sleeve is torn from top to bottom," said Mr. Richmond. "What scratchy things bramble bushes are ! "

"Never mind, Dad," said Alan. "Just think of the lovely bramble jelly we're going to have. We must have gathered pounds and pounds ! "

"I'm sure there isn't a bramble in the Bible," said Margaret with a twinkle in her eye. "I've caught you this time, Daddy ! "

"Oh no, you haven't ! " said her father. "There is certainly a bramble, though perhaps it isn't the same kind of bramble as we find in Scotland. There's a story in the Old Testament which we might call : ' The Bramble who would be King '."

"It sounds like a fairy tale ! " exclaimed Margaret. "Go on, Daddy."

"It is really a parable," said Mr. Richmond. "It belongs to a troubled time in the story of the children of Israel. As often happened, they were quarrelling among themselves. One cruel man wanted to be king, but first of all, he wanted his brothers out of the way. So he hired a gang of rascals to kill all his brothers and leave him free to make himself king. Only one of his brothers escaped, the youngest of them all, called Jotham. He ran away and hid. And so the cruel man became king.

"When Jotham heard this, he came out of hiding and stood on the hill-side where the people could hear him. Then he called to them.

"' I'll tell you a story,' he said. ' You can take its meaning for yourselves.

83

"'Once upon a time the trees decided to choose a king for themselves. First they went to the olive tree and said : 'Reign over us.' But the olive refused. 'Why should I give up my rich oil to be a king ? ' he said.

"'Next they went to the fig tree. But he also said no.

"'Why should I give up my sweet, good fruit to rule over the trees ? ' Then they went to the vine. But the vine, too, refused.

"'At last all the trees went to the bramble, and said : 'Come and reign over us.' And the scratchy, scrubby little bramble bush, full of pride at being asked, said : 'If you really want to make me king, then all of you come and shelter under my branches. But if you are deceiving me, fire will blaze out from my branches and burn even the stately cedars ! ' "

"How silly to think that the bramble could be king of the trees ! " said Alan.

"Yes, that's what Jotham meant," replied his father. "How foolish of the people to make his cruel big brother king."

"And was he a bad king ? " asked Margaret.

"A very bad king," said her father. "He paid no attention to the ways of God, but went on his own way. So you see, Jotham was right. You can't make a king out of a scratchy bramble bush ! Now, I wonder, can you tell me the name of the ' bramble king ' ? "

CHAPTER FORTY-ONE

THE BURNING BUSH

M ARGARET stood at the window and peered out into the darkness. "Look!" she called out suddenly. "The hillside is on fire!"

Her father and mother and Alan came and stood beside her. "I'll turn down the lamp," said Mr. Richmond, "then we'll see better."

As the light in the room grew dim, the blaze outside seemed brighter than ever.

"They're burning the heather," said Alan. "Jim Cameron told me that they do it every year about this time. It must be very dry. Look at the flames shooting into the sky!"

"Listen!" said Margaret suddenly. "I can hear the fire crackling. What a fierce sound it is! I'm sorry for all the wild things, the rabbits and the birds. They'll be homeless to-night."

"I hope it won't spread too far," said Mr. Richmond anxiously. "There's a plantation of valuable young trees on the other side of the hill. A fire like this can do a lot of damage if it is not controlled."

"I expect the foresters are watching it," said Alan. "If the wind doesn't change, their trees should be quite safe."

Margaret drew the curtains close together, while her father turned up the lamp again.

"The burning of the heather reminds me of another Bible story," he said, as they all settled down by the fireside once again. "It is about a shepherd who saw a fire on a mountain-side. At first he thought nothing about it. A bush was on fire, but that was a common enough sight under the blazing heat of the Eastern sun. But the amazing thing was that, though the bush was covered with flames, it was not consumed. The fire burned steadily on.

"'I must go and see this strange sight,' said the shepherd to himself.

"As he went, staff in hand, towards the bush, a voice suddenly spoke to him from the midst of the flames. The voice called him by name. And the shepherd realised that it was the voice of God. God said : ' Come no nearer, but take off your shoes, for the place whereon you are standing is holy ground.' And the shepherd drew his cloak across his face, for he was afraid to look on God.

"The voice came again from the burning bush. ' I have seen the troubles of my chosen people,' God said. ' I am come to deliver them from their cruel masters, the Egyptians. And I have chosen you to be their leader when they escape from Egypt. You will lead them out into a good and large land, a land flowing with milk and honey.'

"The shepherd was greatly distressed. ' Who am I ? ' he said, ' that I should be able for this great task ? '

"And God said : ' Certainly I will be with thee, and the day will come when thou shalt worship on this very mountain.' "

"I know about the land flowing with milk and honey," said Alan. "That was Canaan."

"And what about the shepherd-leader ? " said his father. "Who was he ? "

CHAPTER FORTY-TWO.

THE LOVELY PERFUME

MARGARET dipped her hand into the bowl of dried rose-leaves that stood on top of the book-case. The perfume of roses filled the room.

"What a lovely scent ! " said Mr. Richmond. "It reminds me of the garden in midsummer."

"Yes, the roses *were* beautiful last summer," said Mrs. Richmond. "And they lasted far into the autumn. It's only a few weeks since I gathered these petals. Now we shall have the fragrance of the garden all through the dark winter."

"I expect Dad will be telling us a Bible story about roses to-night," said Alan. "That is, if there are any roses in the Bible, of course ! "

"Oh, yes, we find the rose mentioned in the Bible," said his father with a smile. "Surely you have heard of the rose of Sharon ? "

"I have ! " announced Margaret. "It comes into the hymn that we sing when a baby is baptised in church :

' By cool Siloam's shady rill
How sweet the lily grows !
How sweet the breath, beneath the hill,
Of Sharon's dewy rose ! ' "

"Good for you, Margaret ! " nodded her father. "But, as a matter of fact, the bowl of rose-leaves didn't remind me of ' Sharon's dewy rose.' It made me think of a time in the story of Jesus when a whole house was filled with the fragrance of a costly perfume, just as this room is filled with the scent of our rose-leaves.

"It happened just a week before Jesus died," Mr. Richmond went on. "He was on His way to Jerusalem, and He spent a night at a village called Bethany with His friend Lazarus and his two sisters. Jesus had supper with them, and during the meal a strange and beautiful thing happened. As the guests reclined at table, one of the

87

sisters slipped round to where Jesus was and knelt at His feet.

"She held in her hand a beautiful box, filled with a most costly ointment. She broke the box and poured the fragrant oil over Jesus' feet, and wiped His feet with her long hair. And the whole house was filled with the perfume of the ointment.

"At once, one of the other guests objected. Why was the ointment not sold for its full value, and the money given to the poor ? What a waste of the precious oil, to pour it all on Jesus' feet !

"But Jesus turned and rebuked him. 'She has done a beautiful thing,' He said, ' and as long as the world shall last this lovely deed shall be told about her.' "

"She was showing how much she loved Jesus," said Margaret wisely.

"That was it," agreed her father. "Perhaps that woman was the only one who really understood what was in His heart that night, and that He was going to His death on the Cross. So she lavished all her love on Him in that precious gift of perfume. And the words of Jesus about her are still true. Wherever the Bible is read, and wherever His story is told, her beautiful deed is told, too. It is like the perfume of the ointment. The fragrance of that loving act lives on down the centuries ever since that night in Bethany, long, long ago. And I think you should try to find out the name of the woman with the ointment, don't you ? "

CHAPTER FORTY-THREE

THE GIRL AT THE GATE

"WELL, have you found out the name of the woman with the box of ointment?" asked Mr. Richmond, next Sunday evening.

"Yes," said Margaret. "Her name was Mary, and her sister was Martha."

"And the ointment was called spikenard," added Alan. "What kind of thing was that, Dad?"

"It was a very precious oil which was pressed from a herb that grew in Palestine," said his father. "As we know, it had a lovely perfume. Those who could afford to buy it were fond of using it to anoint their heads."

"Just as we get a costly perfume from the oil of roses," added Mrs. Richmond.

"Yes," agreed Mr. Richmond, "and that reminds me. There is another rose in the Bible. 'Rose' is the name of a girl in the New Testament who had a thrilling adventure one night."

Margaret looked puzzled. "I don't remember ever reading about any 'Rose' in the New Testament," she said.

"No, not quite by that name," Mr. Richmond admitted. "She was a Greek girl, and so her name is the Greek word for 'Rose.' I'm sure you will easily find it out for yourselves.

"This is a story of the early days of the Christian Church," he continued. "King Herod was persecuting the followers of Jesus. First he put James to death, and then he shut Peter up in prison. Peter was the leader of the disciples, so the king took great care that he should not escape. Four soldiers were continually on guard over him, two of them outside the door of his cell, and two of them by his side. And to make doubly sure, Peter was chained to the two soldiers in the narrow cell.

"But in the middle of the night there was a sudden blinding light in the darkness of the prison. An angel of the Lord stood before Peter and told him to get up. As he struggled to his feet the chains fell off his arms. He put on his cloak and sandals, and, like a man in a dream, followed the angel out into the open street.

"When Peter realised the miracle that had happened to him, he made straight for the house of his friends in Jerusalem. He knew that they would be awake all night, praying for him.

"The heavy outer gate was locked for the night. Peter stood in the shadows and knocked. At the sound, a servant girl came from the inner court. She did not open the door, for fear that it might be an enemy.

" 'Who is there ? ' she called.

"What a fright she got when she heard Peter's voice in answer ! In her excitement she forgot to open the door. Instead, she ran into the house to tell the others. But no one would believe her. ' You are mad ! ' they all cried.

"But the servant girl was quite, quite sure.

" ' It was the voice of Peter ! ' she insisted.

"The knocking sounded again, louder and more urgently. One and all they flocked to the gate and threw it open. And there was Peter, just as the girl had said."

"How happy they must have been to see him again, safe and sound," said Margaret.

"And how pleased the servant girl must have been that she was right after all ! " added Alan.

90

CHAPTER FORTY-FOUR

A SUNDAY WALK

"OH, I *am* tired!" said Alan, as he stretched himself before the fire. "We walked miles and miles this afternoon, didn't we, Margaret? I know I'll be stiff all over, to-morrow."

Margaret nodded in agreement. "I'm quite stiff already," she said. "We went all the way to Creagan and back. It must have been at least three miles each way."

Mr. Richmond smiled. "More than a Sabbath day's journey!" he said. "The Jewish law, you know, said that no one was to walk more than a short distance on the Sabbath. And 'the Sabbath day's journey,' as it was called, was less than an English mile.

"But there is a story in the New Testament about a much longer walk than that, longer even than your walk this afternoon. It took place not on the Jewish Sabbath, which is our Saturday, but on the first day of the week, which we call Sunday. In fact, we might say that it took place on the first Christian Sunday that ever was, for it was on the day that Jesus rose from the dead.

"Two of the followers of Jesus were walking from Jerusalem to a village called Emmaus. They were very sorrowful. Only three days before they had seen Jesus put cruelly to death. They could not forget it. All the way along the rough path from Jerusalem they talked of all that had happened, going over the sad story again and again.

"As they went along, another traveller joined them, going in the same direction. They were amazed to find that he didn't seem to know what had happened in Jerusalem.

"'You must be a stranger!' they cried. But soon they found that he knew his Bible better than they did, and, as they went along, he spoke of all God's dealings with His people throughout the generations, and of how Christ must suffer.

"The journey which had seemed so long and dreary at

the beginning ended all too soon. But when they reached Emmaus they would not let their companion go. ' Come and stay with us to-night,' they begged. ' See, it is already getting dark.' And so the stranger went in to have supper with them.

"Then a wonderful thing happened. As they sat at their meal, the stranger took bread, and broke it, and shared it with them. And at once they recognised Him! Who do you think it was ? "

"It was Jesus Himself ! " said Alan.

"Of course it was ! " said his father. "And how excited the two travellers were ! They forgot all their weariness, they forgot the long way back to Jerusalem over a rough road in the darkness. They set out at once, hurrying back to the city, so that they might tell the others that they had seen the Lord, that He was risen indeed, and of how they had recognised Him when He broke the bread."

"You haven't told us who the two travellers were," Margaret reminded her father.

"Neither I have," Mr. Richmond agreed. "But only one of them is named in the Bible. We don't know who the other one was. I expect you will want to find out for yourselves the name of one of that pair of travellers who went for a walk on the very first Christian Sunday."

CHAPTER FORTY-FIVE

LAMP-LIGHT

"ONE thing was better in Glasgow," said Alan one winter evening. "We had electric light there. No messing about with oil lamps every night."

"And no candles to light us to bed," added Margaret. "But I like my bed-time candle, Alan. It's a friendly light."

"Well, there can't have been electric light in the Bible, anyway," said Alan, as he watched his father lighting up the big oil lamp which stood behind his chair. A moment later the soft glow of light filled the room. Margaret pulled the heavy curtains across the window to shut out the view of driving sleet. Then the two children curled up before the crackling log fire.

"It's cosy here," said Margaret. "And oil lamps give a soft, friendly light. I think I like them better than electric light."

"I certainly can't find you any electric light in the Bible," said Mr. Richmond, as he drew his armchair a little nearer the fire. "But there are plenty of lamps . . . and candles, too, as a matter of fact.

"When the children of Israel were wandering in the desert God told them to build a holy place for His worship. In it was a candlestick, or lamp-stand, of pure gold, holding seven oil lamps. Every day the lamps were trimmed and fed with oil. And every evening the priest lit the lamps, and they burned with a soft, steady light in God's holy place throughout the night.

"Many years later, there was a young boy who was a servant in the Temple of God. His name was Samuel. One night, when all was quiet, he looked to see that the lamps of God were burning well. Then he lay down to sleep.

"Suddenly a voice spoke in the solemn silence of the Temple, calling the boy by name.

"Samuel started up. 'Here am I,' he said.

"He drew on his coat and ran to the room where the old priest of the Temple slept.

"'Here I am,' he said. 'You called me.'

"But the priest shook his head. 'I called not. Lie down again.' So Samuel went and lay down.

"But again came the voice. 'Samuel!'

"Again the boy ran to the priest. 'Here I am; you did call me.' And again the old man said: 'I called not, my son. Lie down again.'

"Yet again came the call: 'Samuel!' This time the boy was sure, quite sure. And the old priest saw that he really had heard a voice.

"'Next time,' he said, 'you must answer: 'Speak, Lord, for Thy servant heareth.'"

And once more, as Samuel lay listening, the voice spoke: 'Samuel, Samuel.' And the boy replied as he had been told.

"Then, in the quiet of the Temple, under the light of the golden lamps, God spoke to Samuel, and told him of His purpose for Israel."

"You have told us the boy's name, Daddy, so there's nothing for us to find out, to-night." said Margaret.

"Oh, yes, there is!" said Mr. Richmond with a smile. "What about the name of the old priest, the servant of God? Find that out, and next week I'll tell you about candles and candlesticks."

CHAPTER FORTY-SIX

THE CANDLESTICK

"WE'VE found out the name of the old priest of the Temple of God," said Margaret next Sunday. "He was called Eli."

"Quite right!" said Mr. Richmond. "And I said that I'd tell you to-night about candles and candlesticks. They are mentioned several times in the Bible, but I don't think that the people of Israel had candles like ours. They used oil lamps, not wax candles."

"What were their lamps like?" asked Alan.

"They were usually little flat dishes, rather like saucers," his father replied. "At one side there was a kind of spout, to hold the wick. A little oil was put in the dish and one end of the wick was drawn through the spout and lit. It was a very simple lamp. But of course there were much more splendid lamps than that. The seven lamps of the Temple, for instance. They were made of pure gold, you remember. And in the king's palace there would be big and costly oil lamps."

"So whenever we read about candles and candlesticks in the Bible we should really call them lamps and lamp-stands?" asked Alan.

"That's right!" said his father. "And to-night I'm going to tell you what happened by lamp-light in the palace of a king.

"He was king of Babylon, the distant land to which the Jews had been carried off as slaves. One night the king gave a great feast to his lords and ladies. The palace blazed with light, and there was a great noise of talking and feasting.

"Suddenly the king's face paled. His knees knocked together, and he stared in terror at the wall. There, just beyond the lampstand, or candlestick, as the Bible calls it, was a man's hand. The fingers wrote some words on the wall and vanished. But the words remained.

"Silence fell on the glittering throng in the banqueting hall. Then the king started up.

95

"'Bring in the wizards and the wise men at once!' he ordered. 'Whoever can read the writing and tell me what it means will be clothed in scarlet and have a chain of gold round his neck, and shall be the third ruler in the kingdom.'

"But none of the wise men of Babylon could read it.

"The queen heard what was wrong, and came down to the hall. 'Oh king, live for ever!' she said. 'There is one of the captive Jews who is wise with the spirit of the gods. He will be able to read the writing.'

"So the exiled Jew was brought before the king. He, too, was promised rich rewards if he could read what was written on the wall.

"'I do not want your gifts,' the man replied. 'Yet I shall read the writing. It is a message from God. Your kingdom is coming to an end because you have been proud in heart and have not humbled yourself before God.'"

"What happened?" said Margaret.

"It all came true," her father replied. "Now, I wonder if you can tell me the name of the man who read the writing on the wall when all the wise men of Babylon had failed?"

CHAPTER FORTY-SEVEN

THE LOST SHILLING

"SEE what I've found!" said Mrs. Richmond next Sunday evening. From the study cupboard she brought out a small iron dish with a curved handle.

"Oh, Mummy, what is it? Where did you find it?" chorussed Margaret and Alan.

"It's an old oil lamp," said their mother. "The kind that was used in Scotland long, long ago. I found it up in the attic when I was looking for something else last week. I thought you would like to see it, because it is very like the kind of lamp that Daddy was talking about last Sunday."

Alan took it in his hands. "Yes, there's the place for the wick," he said. "And the oil would go in here."

"It must have been rather smoky," said Margaret, as she looked over her brother's shoulder. "And it wouldn't give a very good light."

"People didn't bother very much about lights in those days," said her father. "They went to bed early and got up very early in the morning. This kind of lamp was called a 'cruisie,' and it was found in every cottage in Scotland at one time. It is very like the simple lamp that the Bible folk had in their homes, only theirs was of earthenware, not of iron.

"There is a story about a lamp like this in the New Testament," Mr. Richmond went on. "It tells of a busy housewife who had ten silver shillings. One morning she found that she had lost one shilling. She was very worried. She counted them all over again, but there was no mistake. There were only nine. At once she began to look all round the room. But it wasn't lying about anywhere. Then she lit a lamp, a small oil lamp, just like this one. With the lamp in one hand and a broom in the other, she swept and poked and pried everywhere. And at last, in a dark corner of the room where it had rolled, she found her silver shilling.

"How relieved she was! She rushed excitedly out of

the house, still clutching her coin, and went to tell her neighbours all about it. She went over the whole story once again, how she was *sure* she had ten shillings, how there were only nine when she counted them, how she had searched and searched, and how she had found the missing bit of money at last. Her kindly neighbours rejoiced with her because she was a poor woman and needed every shilling to buy food for her household."

"Why, it could happen to anyone!" cried Margaret, when her father had finished. "That's just how I would hunt for a shilling if I lost one. The Bible is full of stories about real people, isn't it, Dad?"

"Indeed it is!" agreed her father. "And the whole of that story is told in two verses. I wonder if you can find it, and if you know who told it, and why?"

CHAPTER FORTY-EIGHT

COAL

MARGARET and Alan sat cross-legged before the fire, warming their hands at the blaze.

"Look at the blue flames on top," cried Alan all at once. "That's a sure sign of frost ! "

"Well, it's certainly cold enough for frost, to-night," said his mother. "But how do you know that the blue flames mean frost ? "

Alan grinned. "It's an old country saying ! " he replied.

Mr. Richmond chuckled. "Anyone would think, to hear you, that you had lived in the country all your life ! " he said. "Now, what about stirring yourself and putting on some more coal ? We need a good fire on a night like this, especially if your prophecy about frost is coming true."

Alan got up obediently and put a shovelful of coal on to the back of the fire. As he did so, a blazing coal fell into the hearth.

"Careful ! " cried Margaret, jumping up in alarm. "Quick ! Here are the tongs ! "

The burning coal was safely lifted back into the fire, and the two children settled down again on the hearth-rug.

"I don't suppose you can find coal in the Bible, can you, Dad ? " asked Alan.

"Wrong this time ! " said Mr. Richmond. "Coal is mentioned several times in the Bible. In fact, when you lifted up that burning lump with the tongs, I was reminded right away of something that happened to a young man in the Old Testament.

"He was nobly born," Mr. Richmond went on, "and he had been brought up at the court of the king, in Jerusalem. One day, when he was about twenty years old, he went into the Temple to worship. Standing there in the solemn silence he had a wonderful vision. As if in a dream, he saw God seated upon a great throne. Round about him were the seraphs, calling softly one to another across the Temple,

"Each day, for six days, they marched round the city. Then, on the seventh day, the people of Israel rose up very early in the morning. Almost before it was light they had formed their ranks. At the captain's signal they marched, and again the trumpets sounded. Seven times right round the city they went on the seventh day. At the seventh time the captain gave the order to his troops :

"'Shout, for the Lord hath given you the city.'

"What a roar went up ! And what a crash as the wall fell. For, just when the people shouted, the wall of Jericho collapsed on the ground, leaving the city open to the soldiers. God had given the victory over Jericho. And everyone in Israel knew that God was with their captain who had led them in their strange march."

"Who was he ? " asked Alan. "No, I suppose I needn't ask that ! " he added. "We must find out for ourselves. But I do hope that our wall doesn't fall down like the wall of Jericho ! "

CHAPTER FIFTY

THE WALL REPAIRED

"SO our wall hasn't fallen down, after all," said Mrs. Richmond next Sunday night.

"No, but old Mr. Robson had to work at it for three whole days," said Alan. "He told Margaret and me that he was probably the only man left in this part of Argyll who knew how to repair a dry-stone wall."

"Yes, he's a real craftsman," agreed Mr. Richmond. "We were very lucky that he was able to come and repair the wall. And we were lucky, too, that the weather was so good while he was working. Our old wall should stand now for many a day."

"You told us last week about the wall of Jericho falling down," said Margaret. "Now that our wall has been mended, you must tell us a Bible story about a wall being built up!"

"I can do that!" replied her father. "And a very interesting story it is, too.

"It comes from the time when the Jews were in captivity, far from their native land. They never forgot their own country, and even in distant Babylon they sang the songs of their homeland.

"Among the exiles was a Jew who had become the royal cup-bearer, one of the king's most trusted servants. He heard from far-off Jerusalem that the Holy City was broken down, that the walls were in ruins, and the gates burned with fire. The king noticed that he was sad, and asked him the reason. Greatly daring, the cup-bearer asked for leave of absence to go to Jerusalem. The king willingly gave him a few months' leave of absence from his duties. More than that, he helped him on his way by giving him letters to the rulers of the lands through which he would pass on his journey, and also a gift of timber to help in the work of re-building.

"When the man came to Jerusalem, he wasted no time.

He went out secretly by night and rode right round the desolate city, and saw the broken walls and the burned out gates. Then he called all the people together and told them of his plans for the re-building of the walls. All kinds of people had a share in the work, priests, goldsmiths, chemists, rulers and common folk, and men and women from villages far beyond Jerusalem. ' So built we the wall,' wrote their leader, ' for the people had a mind to work.'

"Their enemies attacked them, but that did not stop the work. The leader gave orders that everyone should arm himself. So they builded, each man working with one hand, while the other hand held a weapon. And a trumpeter stood beside the leader ready to sound the alarm if there was any sign of an attack. All day they toiled, from the rising of the sun until the stars appeared. And no man put off his working clothes, except for washing, until the great task was finished."

"That's a good story ! " cried Alan. "It must have been fine to watch the wall rising bit by bit, and to know that everyone had a share in the building of it."

"Well, you will find the whole story in a book by itself in the Old Testament," said Mr. Richmond. "And the book is called by the name of their leader, the king's cup-bearer, because he wrote it all down for us."

CHAPTER FIFTY-ONE

CHRISTMAS

"ONLY six more days to Christmas," said Margaret. "Just imagine! We've been more than a year in Craiglussach already!"

"I feel as if I'd been here for ages and ages," said Alan. "I never want to leave the country, now. I think I'll be a farmer when I grow up. Then I can stay in the country all my life."

"I'm looking forward to Christmas here," said Margaret. "Mr. Macrae, the head forester, said that we could pick our own Christmas tree from the forest. And if the snow comes soon we'll be able to sledge on the hill-side, and there will be skating on the pond, and, oh, all sorts of things. Last Christmas was quiet, because we hardly knew anyone here. But this time we'll have lots and lots of fun. Why, we know every single person in the place!"

"Yes, a village is a good place to be brought up in," said Mr. Richmond. "You remember at the beginning of the year I told you that Jesus was brought up in a village. He was born in a village, too. What a lot of countryside stories we have discovered in the Bible all through the year!"

"Do you think Jesus knew all those Old Testament stories about the birds and beasts and other country things?" asked Margaret.

"Of course He did!" said Mr. Richmond. "He would hear them from His father and mother when He was a little boy, and later He would read them for Himself.

"Humble country folk were the first to come to see Jesus, the very day He was born," Mr. Richmond went on. "On that very first Christmas day of all, there were shepherds out in the fields all night, keeping watch over their flocks to protect them from wild beasts. And suddenly in the quiet night a great light shone on them and they saw an angel before them. The shepherds were terrified. But the angel said: 'Fear not: for behold I bring you good tidings of great joy, which shall be to all people. For unto you is born this day in the city of David a Saviour, which is Christ the Lord.'

"All at once there was with the angel a great host of angels, praising God and saying: ' Glory to God in the highest, and on earth peace, good will toward men.'

"The vision vanished. At once the shepherds determined to go to Bethlehem to see the Lord of Whom the angel had spoken. They found Him there, a tiny, new-born Babe, lying in a manger, with the cattle standing nearby. And they knelt down in the stable and worshipped Him."

"I wonder if the shepherds were like the shepherd at Inverbaan farm," said Alan.

"I expect they were," said his father. "Just like him, caring for their sheep in the same way as he does."

"It's strange to think that Jesus was born in a stable," said Margaret. "I shall remember that when we go to Inverbaan on Christmas Eve. There's a stable there, and a manger, too, just like the very first Christmas."

"Do you remember the name of the village where Jesus was born?" asked Mr. Richmond. "And the name of the village where He was brought up? I expect you do. They are the best-known villages in all the world."

CHAPTER FIFTY-TWO

THE BRIGHT AND MORNING STAR

"DADDY! Mummy! Alan! Come and look at the stars!" Margaret stood on tip-toe at the doors of the Manse and gazed at the sky. The others came out as she called.

"Look how bright they are," said Margaret excitedly. "Why, there are thousands and thousands of them! I never saw so many before!"

"We never saw them at all in Glasgow," said Alan.

"But they were all there, just the same," said his father, "only the street lights and the smoke and fog made them seem dim. And perhaps you never took time to look for them?"

"I expect that was it," Alan confessed. "How I wish I knew all their names!"

"Why not learn?" said his father. "You will find it very interesting. But you must come in now. It's far too cold to be standing here star-gazing. There's frost coming. The brightness of the stars can tell me that!

"There's quite a lot about the stars in the Bible," Mr. Richmond went on, as they settled themselves round the cheery study fire. "The Jews were great star-gazers. David the shepherd-boy must have watched them often when he was out on the hills at night with his sheep. He wrote a Psalm about them, remember?

'When I consider thy heavens, the work of thy fingers,
The moon and the stars, which thou hast ordained;
What is man, that thou art mindful of him?
And the son of man, that thou visitest him?
For thou hast made him a little lower than the angels,
And hast crowned him with glory and honour.'

"Jesus was born under a wonderful new star," Margaret broke in. "The star that led the Wise Men to Bethlehem."

"Jesus Himself was called a star," said Mr. Richmond. "The bright and morning star . . . one of the loveliest of His names. It was a prisoner who called Him that.

107

Like many other followers of Jesus, he was imprisoned by a cruel Emperor. Many of the disciples were put to death. Others were cast into prison, or made to work as slaves. This man was sent to toil in a quarry, shaping heavy stones that tore his hands and bent his back. And all the world seemed to get darker and darker because of the cruelty and evil of the Emperor.

"Then, in the midst of his slavery, this man had a vision of the glory of God. He saw that all the world was in the hands of God and that He cared for His loved ones. And the weary prisoner heard the voice of Jesus speaking to him. 'I am the bright and morning star,' He said. So the man wrote down all his vision to give his fellow-Christians new hope. We still read his book in our Bible to-day. I wonder if you know who the prisoner in the quarry was, the man who called Jesus the star of hope in a sad world . . . the bright and morning star?"

ANSWERS

ANSWERS

	Answer.	*Reference.*
28.	Andrew.	St. John 6, v. 5-13.
29.	Solomon.	1 Kings 8, v. 22-40.
30.	Naaman.	2 Kings 5, v. 1-5.
31.	Elisha.	2 Kings 5, v. 6-15.
32.	Simon Peter.	St. John 13, v. 1-17.
33.	Bezaleel and Aholiab.	Exodus 35, v. 20-35 ; 38, v. 8.
34.	David.	2 Samuel 23, v. 14-17.
35.	Job.	Job 13, v. 28.
36.	Simon Peter.	St. Luke 22, v. 33-34, 54-62.
37.	Lydia and Paul.	Acts 16, v. 11-15.
38.	Joshua.	1 Samuel 5, v. 1-12 ; 6, 1-15.
39.	Joseph.	Genesis 49, v. 22.
40.	Abimelech.	Judges 9, v. 6-21.
41.	Moses.	Exodus 3, v. 1-15.
42.	Mary.	St. John 12, v. 1-8.
43.	Rhoda.	Acts 12, v. 1-17.
44.	Cleopas.	St. Luke 24, v. 13-35.
45.	Eli.	1 Samuel 3, v. 1-10.
46.	Daniel.	Daniel 5, v. 1-30.
47.	Jesus.	St. Luke 15, v. 8-9.
48.	Isaiah.	Isaiah 6, v. 1-8.
49.	Joshua.	Joshua 6, v. 1-20.
50.	Nehemiah.	Nehemiah 2, v. 1-8, 12-18 ; 3, v. 1-32 ; 4, v. 17-23.
51.	Bethlehem and Nazareth.	St. Luke 2, v. 8-17.
52.	John.	Revelation 22, v. 16.

Jamieson & Munro, Ltd., Printers, Stirling